COSMOS

COSMOS

An illustrated guide to our solar system and the universe

John Gribbin and Simon Goodwin

This book is dedicated to the memory of
Roger Tayler (1929-1997).

Among many better-known and more important achievements, at either end of his time as Professor of Astronomy at the University of Sussex, from 1967 to 1997, Roger helped to set each of us on the path towards a career in astronomy.

Constable & Robinson Ltd
3 The Lanchesters
162 Fulham Palace Road
London W6 9ER
www.constablerobinson.com

Published by Magpie Books,
an imprint of Constable & Robinson Ltd 2006

Designed by Peran Publishing Services

First published in the UK as Origins (1997) and
Empire of the Sun (1998)
by Constable & Company Ltd

A copy of the British Library Cataloguing in
Publication Data is available from the British Library

ISBN-10: 1-84529-454-8
ISBN-13: 978-1-84529-454-0

Printed and bound in China

1 3 5 7 9 10 8 6 4 2

CONTENTS

ACKNOWLEDGEMENTS

Thanks go to Bernd Aschenbach, Jennifer Ash-Poole, Ed Bell, Dave Leisawitz, Gary Linford, Jim Peebles, Jim Sahli, Steve Snowden and Peter Thomas for pictures and help with finding the right ones and also to Jonathan Gribbin, Ian King and Jeremy Maris for help with image processing. Thanks for information to Anne Green, Paul Roche and Andrew Liddle.

AUTHOR'S NOTE

This book follows the standard scientific practice in using the (American) billion to mean a thousand million (1,000,000,000) not the (British) billion of a million million (1,000,000,000,000).

Distances across the Solar System are usually given by astronomers in terms of the average distance between the Earth and the Sun, which is defined as one astronomical unit (1 AU). In round numbers, 1 AU = 150 million kilometres (about 93 million miles). Since light takes 499 seconds to cover this distance, this distance can also be referred to as 499 light seconds, or 8.3 light minutes.

At the risk of irritating our astronomical colleagues, however, we have also given distances in light years, the units favoured by science fiction writers, rather than the units usually used by astronomers, parsecs. A light year is the distance that light travels in one year, 9.46 thousand billion kilometres, and using this unit gives at least a hint of just how big the distances we are dealing with are (a parsec, by the way, is 3.2616 light years).

Following a common astronomical usage, we use terms like 'geology' and 'geological' to refer to the study of planets other than the Earth – for example, the geological activity of Venus.

Part One

Origins

Our Place In Hubble's Universe

ORIGINS

Our Place In Hubble's Universe

Over eighty years ago, the American astronomer Edwin Hubble discovered that the Universe is expanding. The dramatic implication of this discovery, which was not fully appreciated for decades, is that, since the Universe is getting bigger, not only was it smaller in the past, but if you go back far enough into the past it must have had no size at all. It must have been born at a definite moment in time, in the Big Bang.

The reason why this discovery was not made sooner was that before the 1920s the telescopes available to astronomers were not adequate to reveal the true scale of the Universe. Hubble made his discovery with the aid of new technology – specifically, the 100-inch (2.5-metre) diameter reflecting telescope on Mount Wilson in California, which began operating in 1918 and was for almost three decades the largest and most powerful telescope on Earth. This instrument – still in use today – is now known as the Hooker Telescope, after the benefactor who provided the funds for its construction.

Hubble himself was quite a character. Born in Marsfield Missouri, on 20 November 1889, he was the fifth of seven children of a lawyer. He studied law himself, graduating from the University of Chicago in 1911, and visiting the University of Oxford as a Rhodes Scholar. During his time at Oxford, he represented the University at boxing, and fought an exhibition bout as an amateur against the French champion Georges Carpentier. He had been offered a

Opposite: Star trails. As the Earth rotates, the stars in the sky seem to revolve round the poles during the night. With a long-exposure photograph it is possible to catch this apparent motion, as in this stunning picture. The backdrop includes the dome of the Anglo-Australian Telescope at Siding Spring, Australia.

chance to turn professional and fight the great champion Jack Johnson, but (surely wisely) turned it down.

Returning to the United States in 1913, Hubble briefly practiced as a lawyer, but soon decided that this was not the career for him, and went back to the University of Chicago to study astronomy. He received his PhD in 1917, and was immediately offered a job at the Mount Wilson Observatory; but America had just entered the First World War, and Hubble volunteered for the infantry. He went off to France to fight, where he was wounded by shell fragments in his right arm. So it was in 1919, at the age of thirty, that he actually began working on Mount Wilson, with the brand-new 100-inch telescope.

Originally built in 1918, the 100-inch Hooker Telescope at Mount Wilson Observatory in the US was the most powerful telescope in the world for nearly thirty years and is still in use today.

Opposite: Edwin Hubble at the 100-inch Hooker Telescope, with which he did much of his most important work.

Before the Hooker Telescope became available, it seemed that the Universe consisted of an island of stars, the Milky Way, floating in a great, dark void. It is an impressive island – modern observations suggest that it is a disk-shaped system, about 100,000 light years in diameter (which means that light literally takes 100,000 years to cross the disk from one side to the other), made up of several hundred billion stars, each more or less the same as our Sun. But it is not alone.

In the early 1920s, using the Hooker Telescope, Hubble established that what appear as fuzzy patches of light in lesser telescopes are, in fact, other islands in space far beyond the Milky Way, but comparable in size (some bigger, some smaller) to the Milky Way itself. The Milky Way system became known as our Galaxy, with a capital G; these other islands in space are called galaxies, with a small g. It is estimated that about fifty billion galaxies are in principle visible to the best modern telescopes, although only a few thousand have yet been studied in any kind of detail. Among other things, that means that there are a minimum of ten thousand billion billion stars (a 1 followed by 22 zeros) in the visible Universe.

Of course, very few of these stars can be distinguished individually. Most galaxies are so far away from us that even the best modern telescopes only show the vast majority of them as fuzzy patches of light. With the Hooker Telescope, Hubble could resolve individual stars in just a handful of the nearer galaxies. But this was a major breakthrough. Because he could identify individual stars in the nearer of the neighbours to the Milky Way, he could measure their distances. There is a family of stars, known as the Cepheids, which vary in a regular way, brightening and dimming in a repeating pattern.

Opposite: The Hubble Space Telescope as it floats away from the shuttle Discovery *after the February 1997 upgrading mission.*

The average brightness of any one of these stars determines the time it takes to run through one cycle of brightening and dimming. So, by measuring the length of the cycle for a particular star, astronomers can work out how bright the star really is; then, by measuring how faint it looks they can tell how far away it is. This is one of the most important techniques in the astronomer's toolkit, and it shows us, directly, that even relatively nearby galaxies lie millions of light years beyond the Milky Way. We see those galaxies by light which left them before the genus *Homo* had been evolved.

This emphasises a dramatic feature of the way we see the Universe. Because it takes light a finite time to travel across space, we see objects further and further away as they were longer and longer ago. Instead of talking about the distance to a remote object astronomers sometimes refer to the 'look-back time'.

A telescope is a kind of time machine, which we can use to get images of what the Universe was like when it was younger simply by looking further out into space. The snag, of course, is that the more distant an object is, the fainter it looks to us, and the more sensitive the detectors used to study the object have to be. But modern instruments are very sensitive indeed. Light travels at a breath-taking 300,000 kilometres per second, but even so there are objects visible to modern instruments which are so remote that we see them as they were not million, but billions of years ago – more of this later.

If Hubble had retired in 1925, he would still be remembered for making one of the most dramatic discoveries in all of science, the existence of galaxies beyond the Milky Way. But he didn't stop there. Over the next few years, working with his colleagues at Mount Wilson, Hubble discovered that all but the very nearest galaxies to us seem to be receding from the Milky Way, and he quickly realised that in fact all the galaxies are receding uniformly from one another, except in cases where near neighbours are held together by gravity in a bound system (similar to the way the planets are held in orbit around the Sun by gravity, and the way all the stars in the Milky Way are held together in the disk-shaped galaxy by gravity). Hubble had discovered that the Universe is expanding, and he did so using one of the most famous, but also one of the most often misrepresented, tools of astronomy – the redshift.

When light from a hot object, such as a star or a galaxy, is split up into the rainbow pattern of the spectrum (perhaps by using a prism), the spectrum is seen to be crossed by distinct, sharply defined lines. Each element produces its own distinctive 'fingerprint' pattern of lines in the spectrum, always at the same wavelengths when studied in laboratories here on Earth. It is the presence of these fingerprints that enables astronomers to work out, among other things, which elements are present in the Sun and stars. But Hubble noticed that the patterns of lines in the spectra of light from other galaxies are all shifted towards the red end of the spectrum, by different amounts. (The colours of the spectrum are, in order, red, orange, yellow, green, blue, indigo and violet; red corresponds to longer wavelengths and violet to shorter wavelengths.)

One way in which features in a spectrum can be shifted bodily in this way is by the Doppler effect, named after the nineteenth-century Austrian physicist Christian Doppler, who predicted it in 1842. It works both for light and for sound. If an object is moving towards you and emits a musical note, the sound waves get squashed together by the motion and you hear a higher note than the one being played. Similarly, if the object is moving away, you hear a deeper note. This version of the Doppler effect is familiar in everyday life from the way the note of the siren on an ambulance seems to deepen as the vehicle rushes past you.

The optical version of the Doppler effect shifts lines in the spectrum towards the blue end of the spectrum if the object is moving away. These blueshifts and redshifts are indeed seen in the light from stars, and at first Hubble interpreted the redshifts of galaxies in the same way – as indicating that they were rushing apart through space, like fragments of a bomb blasted outwards by its explosion.

But what Hubble didn't know when he discovered the cosmological redshift was that the expansion of the Universe had actually been predicted, ten years earlier, by Albert Einstein. And Einstein's prediction, based on his then brand-new general theory of relativity, said that the expansion was not caused by objects moving apart through space (remember, Einstein's equations made this prediction before the nature of external galaxies had been discovered), but by space itself expanding as time passed.

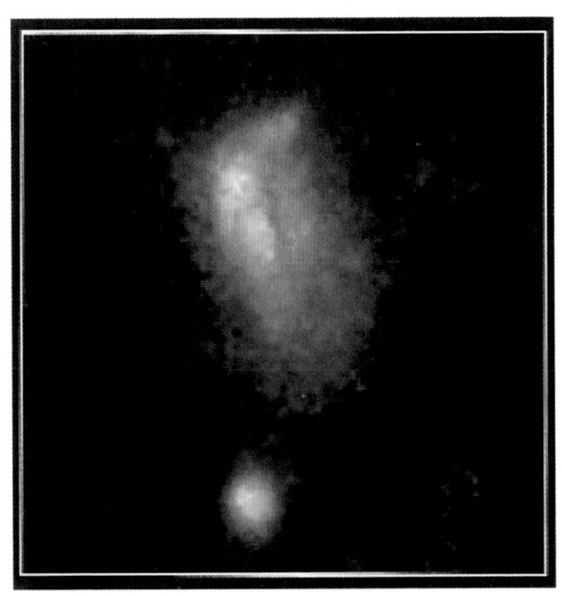

This galaxy is several billion light years away, which means we are seeing it as it was several billion years ago.

When Einstein found that the equations of the general theory had this expansion built into them, he was baffled. In 1917, it was thought that the Milky Way was the entire Universe, and the Milky Way certainly is not expanding. So Einstein added another factor to his equations, a new term, the cosmological constant, dropped in simply to hold the Universe still. He later described this as the biggest blunder of his career. What the combination of Hubble's observations and Einstein's theory (without the fiddle factor!) actually made clear at the end of the 1920s was that the Universe is indeed expanding, and that galaxies are being carried along for the ride as the space between them stretches, stretching the wavelengths of lines in the spectra of those galaxies as the light travels through expanding space on its way to us. The cosmological redshift is not a Doppler effect, and it does not mean that the Big Bang was an explosion involving a lump of matter sitting somewhere in the expanse of empty space; space itself began expanding in the Big Bang, and at no time was there ever anything 'outside' the explosion.

A useful way to picture what is going on is to imagine a fat piece of elastic, or a rubber band, on which you make marks with a biro. If you stretch the piece of elastic, every spot you have marked gets further away from every other spot; but none of the spots is moving through the elastic. The elastic corresponds to empty space, and the way that space stretches is described by the general theory of relativity.

Although the redshifts in the light from distant galaxies are not caused by the Doppler effect, they can still be thought of as due to motion of some kind. So they are usually measured in terms of velocity – a galaxy with a redshift of 100 km/sec, for example, is receding from us at that speed, because the space between us and that galaxy is expanding at that speed. But how far away would such a galaxy be? The crowning achievement of Hubble's career came at the end of the 1920s, when a series of painstaking measurements of both the distances (using primarily the Cepheid technique) and the redshifts of nearby galaxies showed that the redshift of a galaxy is proportional to its distance. In other words, a galaxy twice as far away from us is receding twice as fast. This is exactly the kind of expansion predicted by the general theory of relativity, and it is the only kind of expansion that would look exactly the same whichever galaxy you happen to be living in.

There is nothing special about the Milky Way, and observers in any other galaxy will also see the same pattern, of universal expansion with redshift proportional to distance. All of this was discovered by Edwin Hubble, which is why it is appropriate to describe the Universe we live in as Hubble's Universe.

The key to the Universe was the measurement of the relationship between redshift and distance. Once that crucial number, now known as Hubble's constant, was determined, the distance (and look-back time) to any galaxy could be determined simply by measuring its redshift. Measuring redshifts is relatively easy; the difficult part of the job was measuring distances to enough galaxies accurately enough to determine the value of Hubble's constant. There is still some uncertainty in the exact value of this number, but the uncertainty is getting smaller every year, as new observations are made. We have been involved (together with Martin Hendry, of Glasgow University) in one attempt to measure the Hubble constant, appropriately using data from the Hubble Space Telescope, also named in honour of Edwin Hubble. The calculations we made resulted, in 1997, in a figure of 55 km/sec/Megaparsec (close to the figure other scientists have come up with using different techniques), which means that a galaxy 1 Megaparsec (about 3.25 million light years) away is receding at 55 km/sec, while a galaxy 2 Megaparsecs away is receding at 110 km/sec, and so on. In fact, of course, astronomers use this relationship the other way round; they

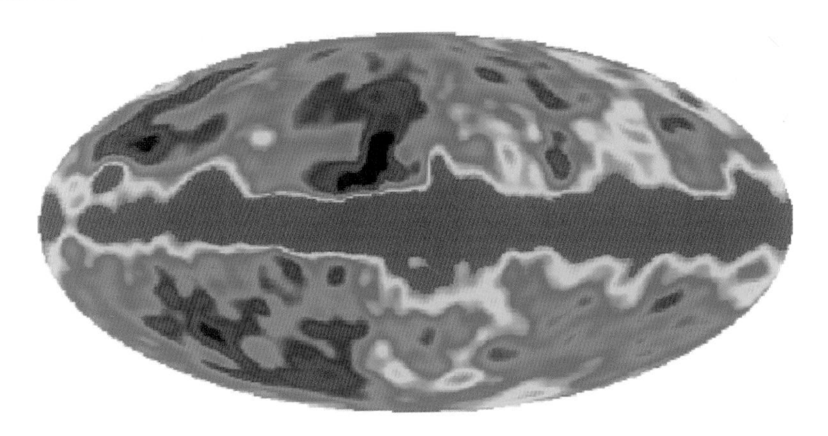

COBE all-sky map of the microwave background radiation. The thick red band shows the position of the Milky Way.

measure the redshift, and use that to work out how far away a galaxy is.

This doesn't just give us a distance scale for the Universe – it also tells us its age. The Hubble constant tells us how fast the Universe is expanding, so it also tells us how long it has taken to expand to the present size since the Big Bang. The smaller the value of the Hubble constant, the older the Universe must be, because it would have taken longer to expand this much. For a Hubble constant of 55 km/sec/Megaparsec, the Universe cannot be more than 18 billion years old. In fact, Hubble's constant is not really constant, because the rate at which the Universe is expanding must have slowed down as time passed, because gravity is trying to pull everything back together; so it was expanding more rapidly when it was younger, and won't have needed quite so much time to reach its present size. Once allowance is made for this, the true age of the Universe must be between 12 billion and 15 billion years. In case you have been misled by some of the more sensational (and less accurate) newspaper accounts of these investigations, we should perhaps mention that this does indeed mean, as you would expect, that the Universe is older than the oldest known stars in the Universe. We shall use a figure of 15 billion years as a rough estimate for the age of the Universe.

Some 15 billion years ago, everything we can see in the Universe (all those fifty billion or so galaxies) was packed into one superdense, superhot fireball, the Big Bang. If you imagine winding the present expansion backwards to its most extreme beginning, it would imply that the Universe appeared out of a mathematical point, a singularity. Nobody believes that that is really what happened, and a new understanding of physics will be needed to explain what happened at the very beginning of time (the implications, beyond the scope of this book, are discussed by John Gribbin in *In The Beginning*). But if we set that hypothetical moment as time zero, where (or when) can we begin to apply standard physics, the kind that has been tried and tested in experiments in laboratories and using 'atom smashing' machines here on Earth? If you make the calculation of how the density of the Universe has declined as it has expanded, then wind that calculation backwards mathematically, you find that just one ten-thousandth of a second after time zero everything in the visible Universe today was packed together in a sphere about one-sixth of a light year across, at the density of the nucleus of an atom (one hundred thousand billion times the density of water) and at a temperature of one thousand billion degrees C. The standard model of the Big Bang tells us, at least in outline, about everything that has happened since – the origins of stars and galaxies, planets, and even people. It tells us about our place in Hubble's Universe.

Until the 1960s, this picture of the Big Bang was not taken entirely seriously. Cosmologists made the calculations, and compared them with observations, and got the right answers. But somehow, nobody really felt in their bones that the calculations were giving a picture of the real Universe. There were only about a dozen cosmologists around, anyway, and they treated the calculations as a kind of game, like cosmic chess, an intellectual exercise rather than an investigation of where we came from. Their eyes were opened to the reality of what the equations were telling them by the discovery of the cosmic microwave background radiation, the echo of the Big Bang itself.

This radiation had actually been predicted back in the 1940s, but the prediction had been forgotten. With the aid of his students, the Ukrainian-born American George Gamow (an ebullient character who was possibly the only cosmologist of his generation to really believe that the equations did indeed describe the birth of the Universe) had calculated what would have happened to the energy of the primeval fireball as the Universe expanded and cooled. The calculation is relatively simple. It says that by about 300,000 years after time zero the entire Universe would have been filled with radiation (essentially, light) at a temperature of a few thousand degrees, roughly the same temperature as the surface of the Sun today. As the Universe expanded, this radiation would have cooled down (one way of looking at this is to think of the radiation that filled the Universe being redshifted to longer and longer wavelengths as the Universe expands). Gamow and his colleagues calculated, some fifty years ago, that by now the Universe would still be filled with radiation, but that the radiation would have been cooled (redshifted) so much that is would have a temperature of about minus 270 degrees C, and would be in the form of cool microwaves, the kind of radiation that would be produced by a very feeble radar transmitter, or by an extremely cold microwave oven.

In the early 1960s, two radio astronomers, Arno Penzias and Robert Wilson, were working with a new antenna at the Bell Laboratories in New Jersey. This instrument had been designed and used in early experiments with satellite communications, and the astronomers were refurbishing it and setting it up to use for radio astronomy. Penzias and Wilson were baffled to find their new telescope plagued by a kind of interference, a weak hiss of radio noise, coming from all directions in space, with a temperature of -270 degrees. They had never heard of Gamow's prediction, but when their discovery was announced in 1965 the connection soon became clear. It was the discovery of the cosmic microwave background radiation that forced what few cosmologists there were to take seriously the idea that there really was an early Universe, and which encouraged many physicists to climb aboard the cosmological bandwagon. The combination of theory and observations fits together so beautifully that it simply cannot be ignored, and must be revealing a deep truth about the nature of the Universe we live in.

One of the greatest achievements of human thought has been the development, over the past seven decades (but especially over the past three decades), of this understanding of how the Universe evolved from a superhot, superdense state – the Big Bang – into the state we see it in today. Using the known laws of physics, studied in laboratories here on Earth, and comparing these with the predictions of Albert Einstein's general theory of relativity, astronomers can calculate how an expanding Universe filled with hot gas cooled, and how that gas condensed to form stars and galaxies, planets, and, ultimately, ourselves. For many years, the observations used to back up these theories consisted largely of fuzzy photographs and squiggles produced by electronic detectors, largely incomprehensible to the lay person, and downright dull as images. But now all that has changed. The latest generation of detectors produces beautiful images from deep space that show the process described by these theories at work, and which stand out as stunning works of art, regardless of their scientific importance.

The archetypal example of such a detector is the Hubble Space Telescope, which has provided so many glorious pictures of the

Universe that they formed the subject of a previous book (*Hubble's Universe* by Simon Goodwin). But there are other equally impressive images, and we have gathered some of them together here. Some come from satellites orbiting above the Earth's atmosphere – satellites such as COBE, the Cosmic Background Explorer, which provided an image of the afterglow of the Big Bang, a view of the Universe almost unimaginably far back and far away – just 300,000 years after time zero. Space probes have

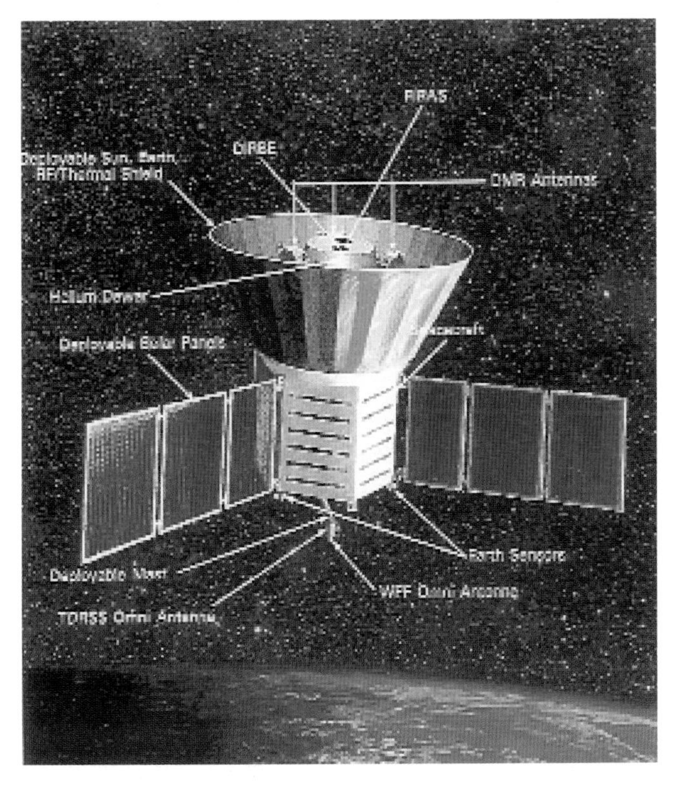

An impression of the Cosmic Background Explorer satellite in orbit. COBE was launched in 1989 and the mission finished after four years, when the coolant required for two of the three instruments finally ran out.

sent back images closer to home, of the planets and other objects in our own Solar System, which shed new light on the processes by which the planets (including the Earth) formed. And ground-based telescopes, continually being upgraded with improved detectors, have provided images in the middle ground – of galaxies and stars being born. Many of the images we have used to tell this part of the story come from the Anglo-Australian Telescope, a 3.9-metre diameter reflector sited 1,150 metres above seal level on Siding Spring Mountain in Australia.

But we have not forgotten the Hubble Space Telescope itself (the HST), which continues to provide some of the most spectacular views of deep space. Launched in April 1990, the HST initially suffered severely from a kind of astigmatism, caused by its main mirror, 2.4 metres across (roughly the same size as the Hooker Telescope that Hubble himself worked with) having been incorrectly manufactured. It was only after a repair mission at the end of 1993 that, as was explained in Hubble's Universe, the telescope was able to function properly, producing the pictures of deep space that made a whole generation of non-astronomers aware of the new understanding of the Universe. In February 1997, a routine servicing mission visited the HST once again, replacing some of its old instrumentation and adding new instruments, including the Near Infrared Camera and Multi-Object Spectrometer (NICMOS), to probe the Universe at wavelengths longer than those of the red part of the spectrum, beyond the range visible to human eyes.

To give you some idea of the value of this kind of upgrade, remember that the original instrumentation for the HST was based on designs from the early 1980s. The upgrade is like replacing an original IBM PC (first put on the market in 1981) with the latest state-of-the-art Power Macintosh. These improvements kept the HST itself functioning as a state-of-the-art machine into the twenty first century, with upgrading missions in 1999 and

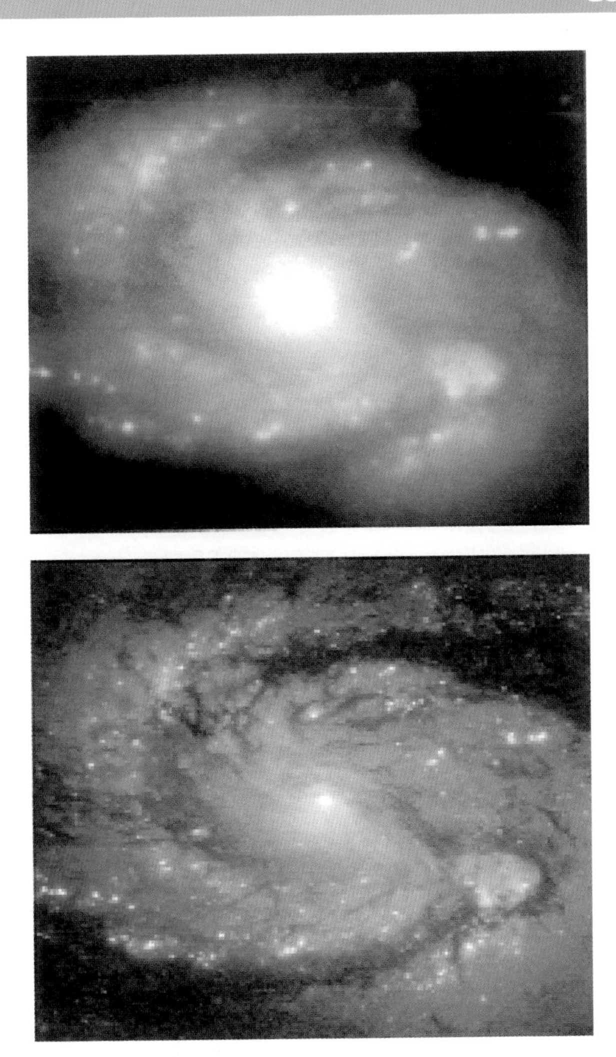

Images showing the vast improvement in the Hubble Space Telescope's power after the 1993 repair mission, when a new instrument was added to the satellite to correct the flaw in the main mirror. The upper picture shows a blurred image of the spiral galaxy M100, before the repair, and the lower one shows the spectacular results that could be achieved after the repair.

2002. A planned servicing mission in January 2004 was cancelled because of concerns following the *Columbia* shuttle disaster in February 2003. The aim of each mission is to extend the telescope's life by five years.

Already, though, astronomers are looking even further into this millennium. Outline plans have been drawn up for several different kinds of Next Generation Space Telescope (NGST), one of which is planned for launch early this century. It is the success of the HST that has convinced the holders of the purse strings that this will be a good investment for the taxpayer's money – an estimated $500 million to build and launch the NGST, and $400 million more to operate it for a decade. Other probes planned include a mission originally known as COBRAS-SAMBA (from Cosmic Background Radiation Anisotropy Satellite/Satellite to Measure Background Anisotropies), but given the simpler but less informative name Planck Explorer. This satellite is due to be launched in 2007, and will map the cosmic microwave background radiation in unprecedented detail. And there are still new telescopes being built on the ground. With the help of lighter materials for their construction, and better computers to steer them and analyse their observations, these are larger and more powerful than Hubble could have dreamed. For example, the Keck Telescope on Mauna Kea, in Hawaii, has a mirror 10 metres in diameter, made up from 36 separate hexagonal mirrors, each 1.8 metres across, which fit together in an array like a slice through a honeycomb, and are steered by computers to work together as if they were one big mirror.

Not that you always need such sophisticated equipment to produce a pretty picture of heavenly object. Astronomy is just about the last area of science where amateurs can, and do, still make important contributions, and just for fun we include here a picture of Comet Hyakutake taken with an ordinary 33-mm camera using a 50-millimetre lens – but, admittedly, a photograph

Comet Hyakutake. This photograph shows that you don't need hundreds of millions of dollars' worth of satellite to obtain a good astronomical picture. It was taken by Luis Chinarro at the Observatorio del Teide in Tenerife with a 50-mm lens on a normal camera, using normal film and a 10-minute exposure time.

taken from an observatory in the clear air of a mountain top on Tenerife.

By putting images from different sources together, and with the aid of the phenomenon of the look-back time, we are able to tell a coherent story, providing an illustrated history of the Universe from the Big Bang to the present day. Using an array of telescopes and detectors, some based on the ground and others orbiting in space, astronomers have been able to obtain images of the Universe in all its stages of development, providing the definitive answer to the age-old question of how we come to be here at all.

The story is spelled out in detail, step by step, in the images and accompanying text which form the heart of this part of the book. But in order to set the scene, we'd first like to give you an overview of the modern understanding of how a sea of superhot gas, expanding out of the Big Bang and cooling as it did so, has given rise to galaxies, stars, planets and people.

The story begins one hundred-thousandth of a second after time zero, when conditions in the entire Universe resembled the activity that goes on in particle accelerators today when beams of particles (such as protons) are smashed head on into one another. Because those conditions can be studied, if only in a limited way, in experiments today, physicists are confident that they know what went on in the early stages of the Big Bang, and how particles such as protons, neutrons and electrons (the building blocks of ordinary atomic matter) interacted at that time. Their calculations say that, by the time these interactions stopped, and the Universe had cooled to the point where stable atomic nuclei could exist (about four minutes after time zero), three-quarters of the atomic matter in the Universe should have been in the form of hydrogen (the simplest element). Lo and behold, when astronomers study the composition of the oldest stars, which

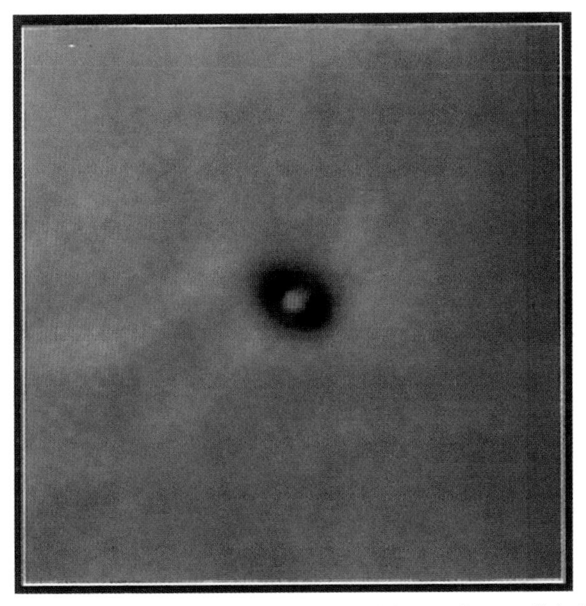

A star in the Orion Nebula surrounded by a dusty disk in which planets are forming.

formed soonest after the Big Bang, they find that they are indeed made up of 25 per cent helium and 75 per cent hydrogen.

But stars did not begin to form until millions of years after time zero. Structure in the Universe grew out of tiny irregularities that were left over from the Big Bang, ripples which left their imprint on the cosmic microwave background radiation. Regions that were slightly more dense than the neighbouring regions had a stronger gravitational pull, because they contained more matter, and this attracted more matter, so that the irregularities grew as the Universe expanded. Huge sheets of gas, hydrogen and helium left over from the Big Bang, began to collapse under the influence of gravity, and broke up to make vast collections of galaxies, smaller clouds of gas collapsed under the influence of gravity to form stars. Heavier elements formed planets.

But this could not have happened if the bright stars and galaxies that we can see were all there is to the Universe. When astronomers try to model the way structure grows in the expanding Universe, using computer simulations, they find that the gravity of all the bright stars and galaxies is not sufficient to do the job. There must be a lot more dark matter, tugging on the bright stuff gravitationally, and holding everything together even though the Universe is expanding. Since this dark stuff cannot be seen, it is not very photogenic, so we cannot show you pictures of it. But the illustrations on pages 43 and 45 show you how the pattern of galaxies in the real Universe compares with the kind of pattern that the computer modellers come up with if they allow for the presence of a hundred times as much dark matter as there is bright stuff. The visible Universe is actually much less than the tip of the proverbial iceberg.

Within a galaxy like our own Milky Way, things would have been pretty dull if all the visible matter had stayed in the form of hydrogen and helium. But the way in which a star generates energy, holding itself up against the inward tug of gravity, is by the process known as nuclear fusion. In the first stage of this nuclear burning, hydrogen is converted into helium, and energy is released. This process is going on inside the Sun today, stopping it from collapsing and keeping it shining. At later stages in the life of a star, helium may be converted into the heavier carbon, carbon into oxygen, and so on. All of the elements in the Universe (except for the original hydrogen and helium) have been manufactured in this way. At the end of their lives, when their nuclear fuel is exhausted, the bigger stars explode, scattering the elements built up inside them (plus many more produced in the explosion itself) across space. Those heavy elements are

Opposite: The Horsehead Nebula: one of the most spectacular examples of a dark nebula seen against the backdrop of a bright emission nebula.

incorporated into clouds of gas and dust in space, from which new stars, laced with heavier elements, can form. Among other things, planets are made out of these heavier elements, and planets – such as Earth, with its iron core – could not exist until the first stars had run through their life cycle in this way.

This is how the Solar System formed. The Sun is a middle-aged star, only some 4.5 billion years old, and formed out of material that had already been partially processed inside two or more generations of preceding stars. Everything in the Solar System, except hydrogen and primordial helium, including the atoms your own body is made of, has been manufactured in this way inside another star.

The origin of our Solar System is intimately related to the structure of the Milky Way galaxy, just as the origin of our Galaxy is intimately related to the structure of the whole Universe. The Galaxy is, as we have mentioned, a disk-shaped system of stars. Seen from above, it would look something like a huge Catherine wheel (or like the galaxy shown on page 71), with tightly wrapped 'spiral arms' of stars winding round the central bulge. The Sun and its family of planets lie about two-thirds of the way out from the centre, towards the rim. Unlike a Catherine wheel, a galaxy like our own does not rotate as a solid body. Individual stars and other objects move in their own orbits, and pass through the spiral arms on their journey round the centre. The spiral arms are features rather like waves on the ocean, through which stars pass all the time.

These spiral arms stand out because they are made up of hot, young stars which shine brightly. The kind of stars forming today – stars like the Sun – form in groups, loose clusters of stars all formed from one large collapsing cloud of gas or dust. And what makes them collapse is their passage through the spiral arms. It may just be the squeeze they get from the pressure wave associated with the arm that does the trick. It is more likely, though, that the trigger for a burst of star formation is the blast wave from a supernova, the explosion of a large star, rippling through the interstellar medium.

Stars of all sizes form in the spiral arms, and the most massive stars live for only a few million years before they explode, seeding the nearby clouds with heavy elements, and also causing some of those clouds to collapse and form new stars. All of this happens within the vicinity of the arms, because those short-lived stars do not have time to move far before they explode.

Because of all the second-hand material around in the cloud from which the Sun formed, it was accompanied by a dusty disk of gas, in which particles of dust collided and stuck together and gradually grew big enough to attract other dust grains by gravity. The lumps grew bigger until they formed the planets, with the last stages of planet formation involving the bombardment of the young planets by huge rocks from space as the last of the debris was swept up. The scars from this terminal bombardment can still be seen today, notably on the faces of the Moon and Mercury.

Some of the material left over from the formation of the Solar System formed a band of rocky debris (the asteroid belt) orbiting between Mars and Jupiter; some formed a cloud of objects orbiting beyond the orbits of the planets, from which one lump is occasionally disturbed into a trajectory that takes it close past the Sun and puts on a temporary, but spectacular, display as a comet.

One of the planets that formed from the swirling disk of dust around the young Sun was just the right distance from the Sun for oceans of liquid water to form and provide a home for life. But every step in the chain, from the Big Bang to life on Earth, depended on the previous step. We are what we are because the Universe is the way it is.

Stars like the Sun, though, live for much longer than the kind of star that forms a supernova, and the story of life on Earth is less than half over. Our Sun is roughly half-way through its lifetime, and has about another 5 billion years of existence in more or less its present state to look forward to. Travelling once around the galaxy every 250 million years, it has already completed the circuit about twenty times. When the Sun has exhausted its hydrogen fuel, after another twenty circuits of the Galaxy, it will spend a short time burning helium into carbon, and its atmosphere will swell up, engulfing the inner planets. Eventually, being too small to form a supernova, it will fade away into a stellar cinder, a cooling lump of star stuff about as big as Earth.

For every step in this story, the match between theory and observation is good, confirming that astronomers really do understand the origins of the Universe and all it contains. The stunning new images which we have selected for this book show the birth-pangs of creation in the Universe at large at each step in the chain. We can now see pictures of events that previous generations of astronomers could only picture in their mind's eye – and which non-astronomers could not even imagine.

What we see confirms that we live in a Universe that was born in a Big Bang, and has been expanding for some 15 billion years, while stars, and planets and people came into existence within it. This is the Universe discovered by Hubble at the end of the 1920s – Hubble's Universe. Our place in Hubble's Universe is as the inhabitants of an ordinary planet, orbiting an ordinary star, in a backwater of a slightly smaller than average galaxy, one of tens of billions of galaxies in the Universe at large. There is nothing special about our place in the Universe – but the view is spectacular.

Origins

Our Place In Hubble's Universe

The Pictures

THE COBE FOUR-YEAR MAP

The most distant view we have across the Universe, and the furthest back in time that we can 'see' towards the Big Bang, is the view provided by the cosmic microwave background radiation. This is actually detected by radio telescopes, both on the ground and on board unmanned satellites such as COBE. But astronomers can use the measurements of the radio noise that fills the Universe to draw a kind of contour map of how the sky would look to us if our eyes were sensitive to this kind of microwave radiation. The colours they use to fill in these maps are in principle as arbitrary as the convention by which the old British commonwealth countries are coloured pink on maps of the world; but the usual convention, as with the COBE image opposite, is to colour regions of the sky that are slightly hotter than average (corresponding to greater density) red, and regions of the sky that are slightly cooler than average (corresponding to lower density) blue.

This image was built up by adding together – in a computer – data obtained over the entire four-year lifetime of the COBE mission. It shows the entire sky, as two hemispheres, in the same way that some flat maps of the Earth show the entire surface of the planet as two hemispheres. The detail shows 'ripples' which reveal the nature of irregularities in the Universe when it was just 300,000 years old. The radiation from those ripples has been travelling through space for some 15 billion years, giving us a snapshot of how the hot gas that filled the Universe at that time was distributed. Those irregularities were so big that they formed the seeds from which not just individual galaxies but huge clusters and super-clusters of galaxies grew – the largest features seen by any optical telescope on Earth would fit within the smallest features seen on this map.

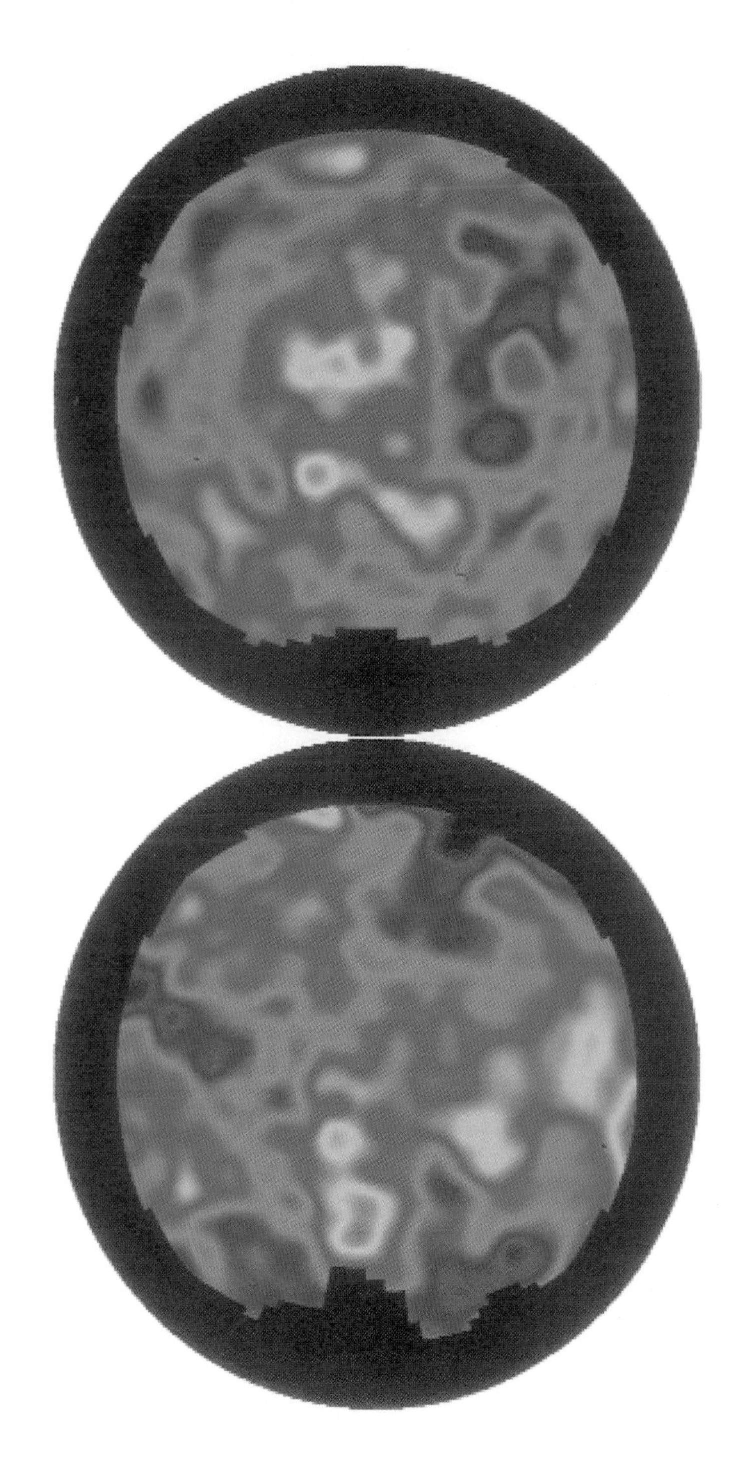

SIMULATIONS OF GALAXY FORMATION

For about a billion years after the time that the background radiation last interacted with matter, the Universe was dark. The first galaxies took time to grow out of the ripples imprinted on the expanding Universe as it emerged from the Big Bang. In order to fill the gap, and to test their theories of how galaxies formed, astronomers use large supercomputers to calculate the way in which ripples like the ones revealed by COBE must have grown. The computer programme calculates how an initially almost imperceptible irregularity gets bigger by attracting surrounding material through its gravitational pull. It cannot use observations of the details of the actual ripples in the background radiation to calculate the formation of real clusters of galaxies because there is not enough detailed information in the observations of the background radiation. Instead, it is based on a pattern of initial ripples which has the same overall statistical properties as the ripples in the real Universe, but an arbitrary detailed structure.

This image is the only one in this part of the book which does not come directly from the real Universe. It shows the result of this process, simulated in a Cray-T3D supercomputer (one of the most powerful computers in the world), which mimics the simultaneous collapse of individual lumps of matter and the expansion of the Universe which separates the lumps. The result is a complex, filamentary structure, with regions of high density stretching in streamers and sheets across the Universe, surrounding large empty voids. According to theory, this kind of structure should have been imprinted on the Universe by the time it lit up, as galaxies and stars started to shine in the densest regions.

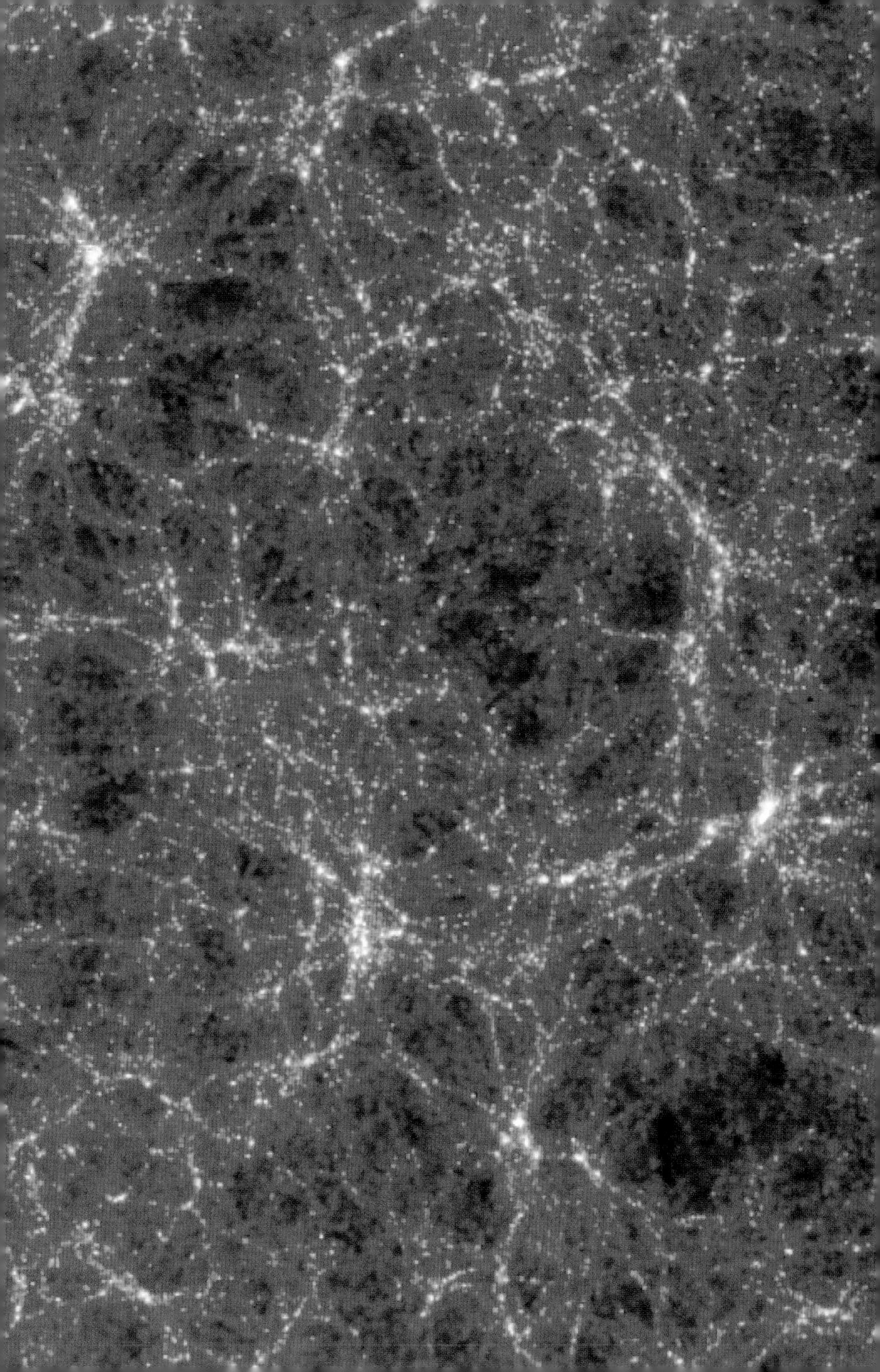

THE LICK GALAXY MAP

One of the most dramatic pieces of evidence that astronomers really do understand the nature of the Universe at large is provided by the match between computer simulations of the growth of structure in the early Universe and what we see on the night sky. By putting together a mosaic made up from many separate photographs taken at the Lick Observatory in California, astronomers at Princeton University compiled this view of the northern hemisphere night sky which contains the images of more than a million galaxies. The scale is so large that you cannot see all the individual galaxies; bright spots in this picture represent clusters of galaxies, which each contain hundreds or even thousands of individual galaxies. The striking bright spot near the middle of the picture, for example, is the Coma Cluster.

The most remarkable overall feature of this portrait of more than a million galaxies is the way in which its overall appearance resembles that of the computer-generated image on page 43. This is confirmation that the computer simulations really do provide a good link between the time when the Universe emerged from the hot fireball of the Big Bang and the time when it settled down into more or less the state we see it in today. To give you some idea of the scale involved, the largest dark voids in the visible Universe are about 250 million light years across. Because light travels at a finite speed, the furthest we can see across the Universe is 15 billion light years, the distance that light has had time to travel since the Big Bang. So an individual void is about one-sixtieth of the size of the observable Universe.

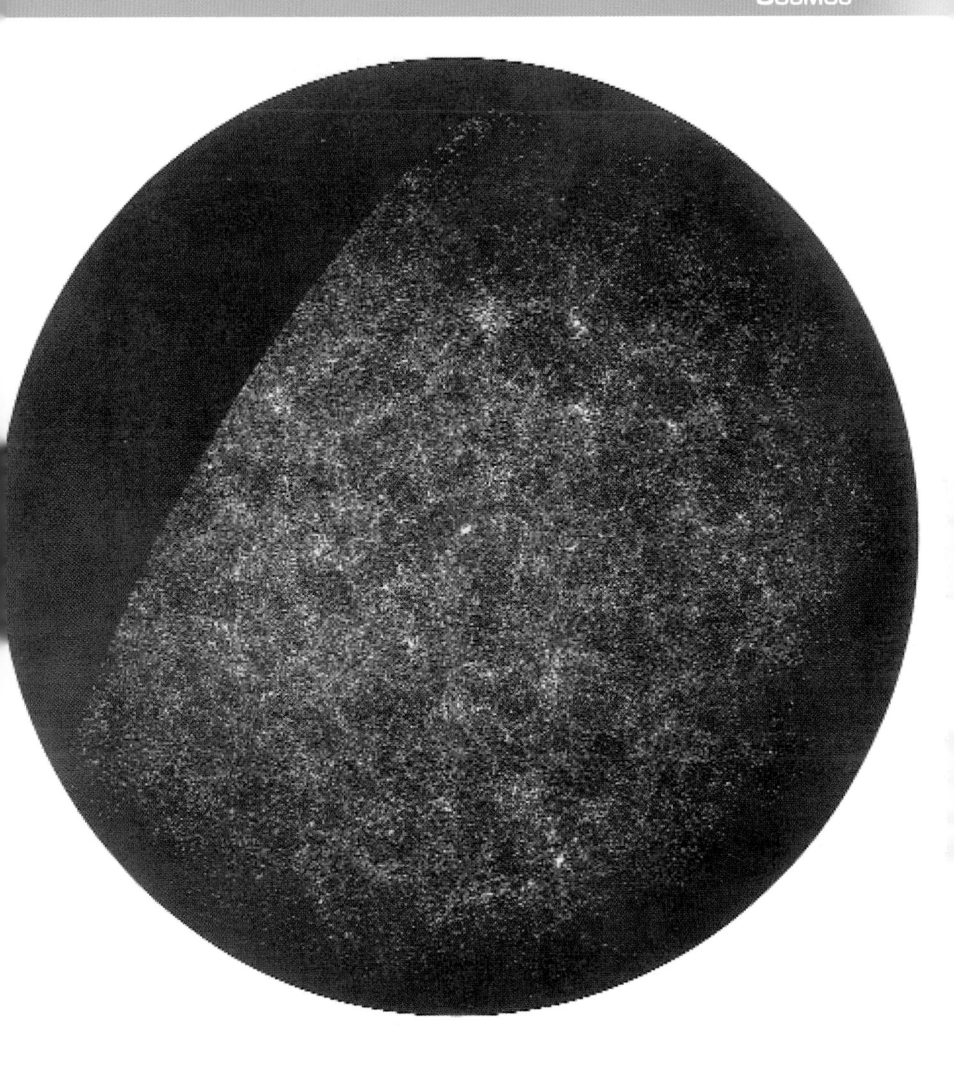

THE COMA GALAXY CLUSTER

Our own origins are intimately connected to the origin of structure in the Universe, because without those ripples in the fireball that grew to become great steamers and superclusters of galaxies there would be nothing in the Universe except a thin gruel of hydrogen and helium gas, getting thinner as the Universe expanded. Even our Milky Way Galaxy; let alone the Solar System, is a tiny detail in the overall structure of the Universe.

Some idea of just how small we are on the cosmic scale comes when we take the first step down from the Universe at large to smaller structures; this brings us to clusters of galaxies like the Coma Cluster. But even the Coma Cluster is made up from more than a thousand bright galaxies, held together by gravity and moving together like a swarm of bees. It is more than 300 million light years away from us, and is being carried further away at a rate of 6,700 km per second by the expansion of the Universe.

One of the best ways to see that the Coma Cluster really is a single system, and not a chance alignment of many galaxies on the sky, is by looking at X-ray wavelengths. X-rays do not penetrate the Earth's atmosphere, and X-rays from space can only be studied by hoisting instruments on rockets and satellites such as ROSAT into space. ROSAT (short for ROentgen SATellite, named in honour of the discoverer of X-rays) was launched in 1990, and carried out a complete survey of the sky at low-energy X-ray wavelengths. As with radio images of the Universe, the X-ray data can be converted into colourful maps, which show how the world would look if we really did have Superman-like X-ray vision. Most of the X-rays from the Coma Cluster come from hot gas between the galaxies, although some individual galaxies show up as bright spots in the image. The concentration of gas towards the centre

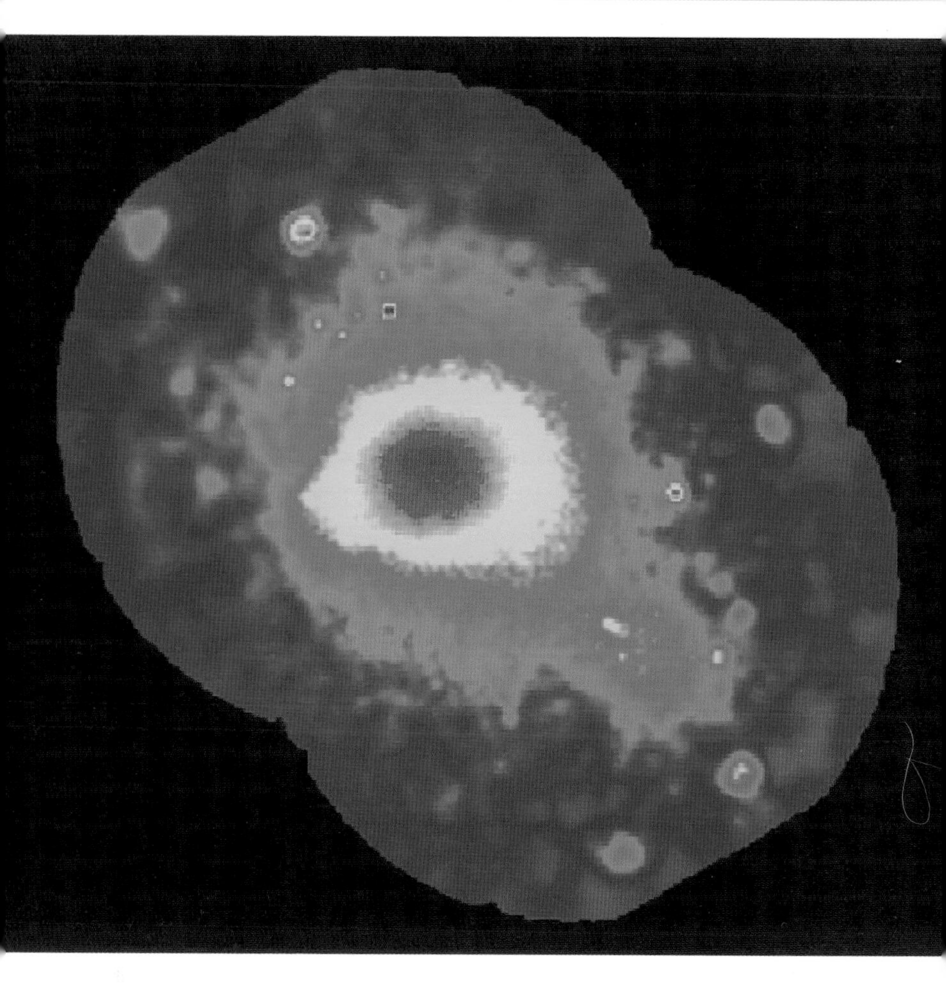

of the cluster shows that the whole system is held together by gravity, forming a kind of gravitational pot-hole, with the gas falling into the centre of the system. The slightly brighter blob in the lower right of this X-ray image shows where a smaller group of galaxies is being sucked in by the gravity of the Coma Cluster, falling into the pot-hole, where it will eventually merge indistinguishably into the cluster.

THE HOMES OF QUASARS

Even when we get down to the scale of individual galaxies, we find that the further back in time we look (that is, the further away across the Universe), the more violent the Universe was. The most extreme individual phenomena that we can see are the quasars. These each shine a thousand times more brightly than all of the hundreds of billions of stars in a galaxy put together, but the source of this brightness is energy from a tiny region, no bigger across than our Solar System. This is what gave them their name, a contraction of quasi-stellar objects, because they look like points of light (like stars) in a telescopic image, but shine far more brightly than any star.

The explanation of this enormous energy output is that each quasar is a black hole, containing perhaps 100 million times as much mass as our Sun. Although this is only a small fraction of the total mass of a galaxy like our own, the concentration of so much mass in a small volume of space creates a gravitational pot-hole with sides so steep that nothing, not even light, can escape from it. In a young galaxy, there is plenty of gas around which has not yet been turned into stars and can fall into this black hole. As material is sucked into the black hole, it forms a swirling ring of matter around it, which is where the energy that powers a quasar is generated, and where sometimes whole stars are ripped apart and swallowed.

The most distant quasars can be seen 12 billion light years away across the Universe, as they were when the Universe was only 20 per cent of its present age, long before the Earth formed. But in spite of their vast energy output, such distant objects are too faint to be very photogenic. The ones pictured overleaf are much closer to us, close enough that the host galaxies in which they are embedded can also be seen. Their distances range from 1.5 billion light years to 3 billion light years from Earth – so the light by which we see the closest one has been travelling for a third of the time the Earth has existed, and the light by which we see the most distant of these six systems has been travelling for two-thirds of the time the Earth has existed. The distorted structure of the galaxies is a result of the tidal forces of the quasars that are gripping them by gravity.

Even closer to home, many galaxies may harbour black holes which used to be quasars, but have gone quiet as the supply of gas and dust falling into them has run out; even our own Milky Way Galaxy has a supermassive black hole at its centre.

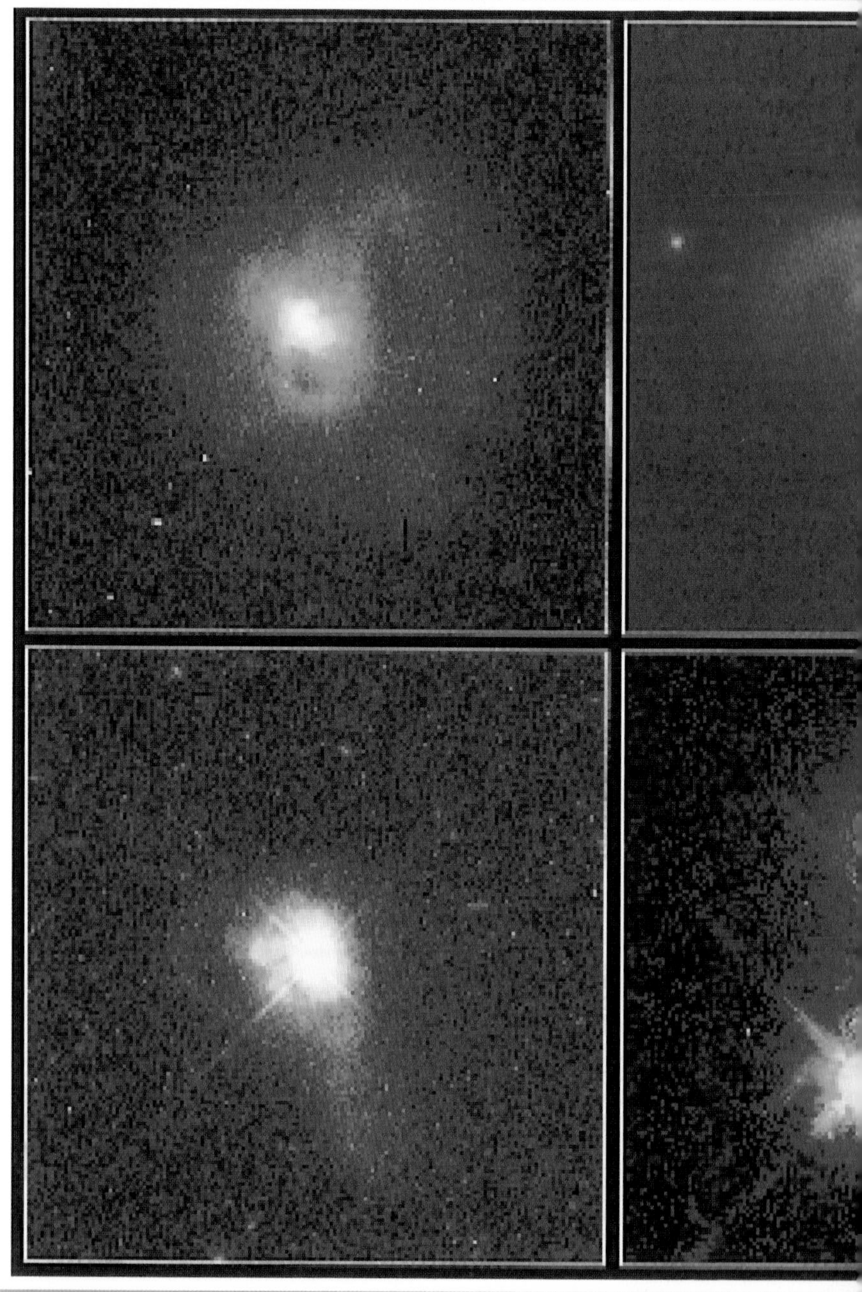

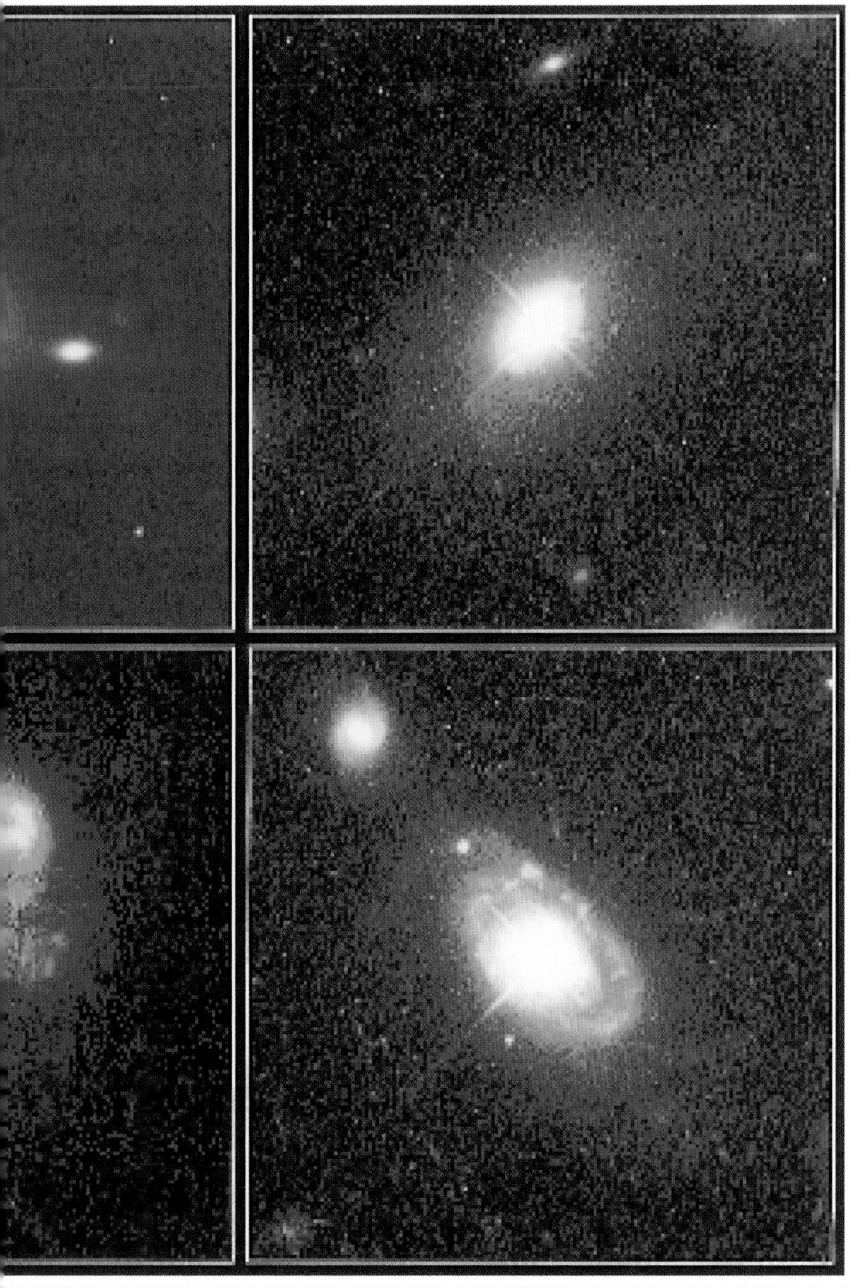

THE HUBBLE DEEP FIELD

The best view we have of very young galaxies in the Universe at large comes from the Hubble Space Telescope, which was used to take 342 exposures of the same patch of the sky, each lasting for between 15 and 40 minutes, on 150 successive orbits of the telescope around the Earth. These 342 exposures were then added together electronically to provide one image of some of the faintest (and most distant) objects ever viewed in the Universe. The Hubble Deep Field Survey covers a tiny portion of the sky, only one-thirtieth of the diameter of the full Moon as seen from Earth. The patch of sky chosen for the survey lies in the direction of the North Galactic Pole, pointing straight up out of the plane of the Milky Way to one of the darkest parts of the sky; but it is thought to be representative of the way the Universe would look in any direction, if the view were not obscured by the Milky Way itself. All of the hundreds of images in the Deep Field are galaxies, some so faint that they may be even more distant than the quasars shown on pages 50 and 51. This means that the galaxies as we see them are very young objects – although the light by which we see them is now nearly as old as the Universe itself. What we see are swarms of irregular galaxies, not yet settled down into the smoothness of middle age, many of them in the process of interacting with other galaxies and merging to form larger systems.

A VERY YOUNG GALAXY

A close-up of part of the Hubble Deep Field image shows the way galaxies interacted in the crowded conditions that existed when the Universe was young.

At distances corresponding to a look-back time of about 5 billion years (to a time just before the Earth formed), galaxies are much bluer than nearby galaxies, which is a sign that star formation was very active then (young stars are hot and blue). Many of the objects in these distant clusters are pairs of disk galaxies, broadly similar to the Milky Way, in the act of merging. Mergers like this produce a huge burst of star formation, using up most of the gas and dust in the merging galaxies.

The merged systems then settle down into the form of smooth elliptical galaxies, which are largely free from gas and dust. About half of all the galaxies we see today have been involved in mergers with galaxies of a similar size within the past eight billion years – roughly the second half of the lifetime of the Universe so far.

Disk galaxies themselves are thought to have formed from mergers between even smaller units very early in the life of the Universe. These small, faint objects are too distant to be seen in the act of merging, even with the HST. But the range of ages of the globular clusters in our own Galaxy (see page 74) is from about 14 billion years to about eight billion years, suggesting that our Galaxy formed over a span of several billion years, from an amalgamation of about a million primordial gas clouds.

The very youngest galaxies, like the one marked by an arrow overleaf, are so far away that the redshift has moved all the blue light from young stars into the red part of the spectrum. These galaxies, which look red to us, are further away than the furthest quasar. They are the most distant individual objects that have yet been seen.

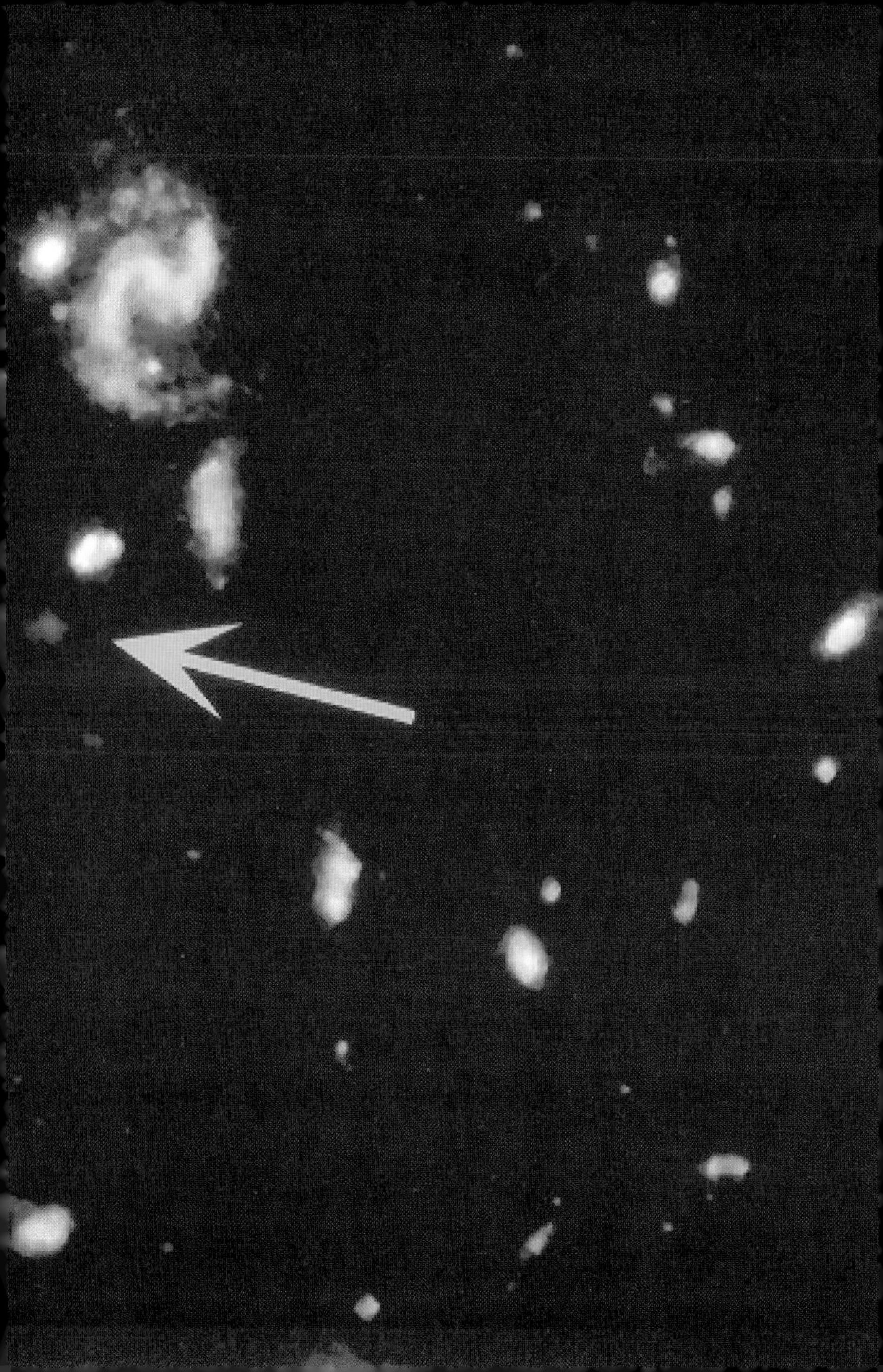

A GRAVITATIONAL LENS

Although very young galaxies are too distant to be imaged in detail by the HST without help, nature sometimes provides a natural enlarging lens which makes some of the detail inside one of these galaxies visible. If there is a large massive object along the line of sight between us and a very young galaxy, the gravity of the massive object can bend light from the even more distant galaxy, acting as a gravitational lens and magnifying the image. The effect was predicted by Albert Einstein, using his general theory of relativity, in the 1930s; but it was not observed until the 1980s.

In this image, obtained using the HST, light from a distant galaxy is being bent as it passes through the cluster of galaxies that can be seen near the centre of the image. The cluster is 5 billion light years away from us; the light from the distant galaxy, which is itself about 10 billion light years away, is bent to form five separate blue images, which have been distorted into arcs by the lensing effect. The blue images are near the centre of the picture, and at 6,7,8 and 2 O'Clock.

The combination of the HST and the natural gravitational lens makes it possible to pick out details as small as 300 light years across in this galaxy 10 billion light years away. This is like being able to read lettering three-hundredths of a millimetre high at a distance of a kilometre. The detail shows that this is a lumpy galaxy in which primordial gas clouds are still merging to form a single system, with a great deal of star formation going on.

ELLIPTICAL GALAXY M87

Elliptical galaxies are the giants of the Universe, huge star systems built from the mergers of smaller galaxies. Although some objects described as dwarf ellipticals each contain only about a million times as much mass as our Sun, these resemble the globular clusters that are associated with our own Galaxy and others. The record-breakers are the giant ellipticals, each of which may contain several thousand billion stars. About 60 per cent of all galaxies are ellipticals, and they are particularly common in clusters of galaxies, where there has been ample opportunity for disk galaxies to collide with one another and merge to form ellipticals. In very rich clusters (ones in which very many galaxies are crowded together), there is almost invariably a huge elliptical galaxy at the centre of the system, where it sits like a spider at the centre of its web, dominating the cluster gravitationally and pulling more of the other galaxies in the cluster into its embrace.

This particular elliptical galaxy is M87 (also known as NGC 4486), one of the largest and brightest ellipticals in the relatively nearby Virgo Cluster of galaxies. Although it looks placid enough, sitting in space surrounded by its own globular clusters, in this picture from the Anglo-Australian Telescope (AAT), spectroscopic studies have shown that at the centre of M87 there is a whirling disk of matter, orbiting at a speed of 550 km per second around a central mass containing three billion times as much matter as our Sun. This can only be a black hole, and may once have been a quasar.

The red appearance of M87 is typical of elliptical galaxies, showing that they are made up of old, red stars. The presence of a central black hole is also probably typical; the most powerful astronomical radio sources are associated with giant ellipticals, and the most likely explanation is that the energy which powers the radio sources comes from matter falling into a black hole.

A FACE-ON SPIRAL GALAXY

The kind of galaxy we live in is much more photogenic than an elliptical, and has a lot more interesting activity going on even in its outer regions today. These are properly known as disk galaxies, because they are flattened, rotating systems; many disk galaxies, like NGC 2997 (photographed here by the AAT) have a beautiful spiral pattern when seen face on, and are also known as spiral galaxies. This is very much the way our Milky Way Galaxy would look if viewed from above; in our Galaxy, the Sun is about two-thirds of the way out from the centre, near one of the spiral arms.

The blue colour of NGC 2997 is typical of disk galaxies. It is caused by the presence of many hot, young, blue stars, which form along the spiral arms. All disk galaxies have a central bulge, dominated by older, red stars, like a miniature elliptical galaxy; the ratio of the disk to the bulge is roughly the same as the relationship between the white and the yolk of a fried egg, and the thickness of the disk is only about one-fifteenth of its diameter. Spectroscopic studies show that in galaxies like this the whole visible system is embedded in cloud of dark matter (perhaps ten times as much as all the matter in the visible bright stars put together), holding the galaxy in its gravitational grip and controlling its rotation, which is always in the direction corresponding to winding up the spiral arms (clockwise in the image shown here).

AN EDGE-ON SPIRAL GALAXY

This is the same sort of galaxy as NGC 2997, a spiral galaxy, but seen edge on. The dusty clouds which provide the raw material for the birth of stars in disk galaxies show up very clearly in this AAT photograph of NGC 4945. Because the Sun and the Earth are located in the disk of our own Galaxy, this is similar to the view we get of the Milky Way from the inside - see pages 80 and 81. About 30 per cent of all galaxies are disk galaxies.

A BARRED SPIRAL GALAXY

Many spiral galaxies, like NGC 1365 (pictured here by the AAT), have bars across their centres, with the spiral arms growing out from the ends of the bar. Computer simulations show that the spiral pattern seen in many disk galaxies would not persist for very long unless it were stabilised by the large halo of dark matter in which the galaxy is embedded. But even with this stabilising influence, the spiral pattern cannot persist forever, and the natural way for the pattern to break up is by the growth of a bar of stars outwards from the centre of the galaxy.

It is likely that our own Galaxy will evolve in this way, and there is some evidence that there is already a small bar of stars across the centre of the Milky Way. But it is very difficult to observe this region of the Milky Way because the view is obscured by all the gas and dust in the disk of our Galaxy.

A STARBURST IRREGULAR GALAXY

Along with the easily classifiable elliptical and disk galaxies in the Universe, there are systems which are irregular in shape and do not fit either category – so they are known as irregular galaxies. About 10 per cent of all galaxies are irregulars, and many of them seem to be undergoing an intense phase of star formation, as in the case of this 'starburst irregular', NGC 1313, photographed by the AAT. Using radio telescopes, astronomers can often find evidence of a disk of gas within such an irregular galaxy. Together with the fact that stars are still being formed in them, this gives irregulars a family resemblance to the disk galaxies rather than to the ellipticals.

Starburst activity (which is also seen in otherwise normal disk galaxies) is often triggered by the tidal pull of a nearby galaxy interacting with the material of the starburst galaxy to produce dense regions of dust and gas which collapse to form stars; but in some cases starbursts seem to be occurring in galaxies that do not have any near neighbours, and we do not know what has triggered the activity (it may be that the galaxy has simply run into a cloud of cold gas between the galaxies, in 'empty' space). The large amounts of gas and dust associated with the star-formation activity make it difficult to see deep into these galaxies using ordinary visible light, but they show up very brightly to infrared detectors.

SPIRAL GALAXY M101

Because we cannot look at our own Galaxy from the outside, it is worth looking at another image which gives a different kind of view of a galaxy very similar to our Milky Way. This is M101, photographed in ultraviolet light by the Ultraviolet Imaging Telescope carried on the Astro-2 mission of the space shuttle *Endeavour*. M101 is only about 16 million light years away from us, making it a relatively near neighbour on the cosmic scale, and its appearance is typical of disk galaxies today.

Ultraviolet light lies beyond the blue end of the spectrum visible to our eyes – it is literally bluer than blue – and because hot young stars produce a lot of blue and ultraviolet light they show up particularly clearly in this kind of image, sharply outlining the spiral arms in M101. The image also highlights huge glowing regions known as HII regions – nebulae which shine because of the ultraviolet energy being produced by the young stars embedded within them. These are the birthplaces of stars.

THE LARGE MAGELLANIC CLOUD

Focusing even closer to home, the same Astro-2 mission, carried out between 2 March and 18 March 1995, brought back this image of a star-forming region in the Large Magellanic Cloud. The LMC is an irregular galaxy which is a close neighbour of the Milky Way, at a distance of just 160,000 light years. It is so close that the light by which we see it left as recently as during the Ice Epoch before last here on Earth.

The bright region of star formation forms a clearly visible arc in this ultraviolet image. It is about a thousand light years long, and contains at least five clusters of very hot massive young stars. Because these stars are so massive, they use up their nuclear fuel quickly and run through their life cycles in only a few million years, many of them destined to explode and scatter heavy elements across the nearby region of space. But within these brightly visible regions there are also stars like the Sun, much smaller and fainter than the blue giants, but destined to have a much longer life, and still be around billions of years from now.

The shape of the arc of star formation may be an indication that it is part of a wave of star-forming activity rippling through the LMC. Such a wave can sustain itself because of the way massive stars quickly run through their life cycles and explode, the blast waves from the explosions squeezing clouds of gas and dust just ahead of the arc and triggering the next burst of star formation. A similar process probably explains the way in which spiral arms are formed in disk galaxies.

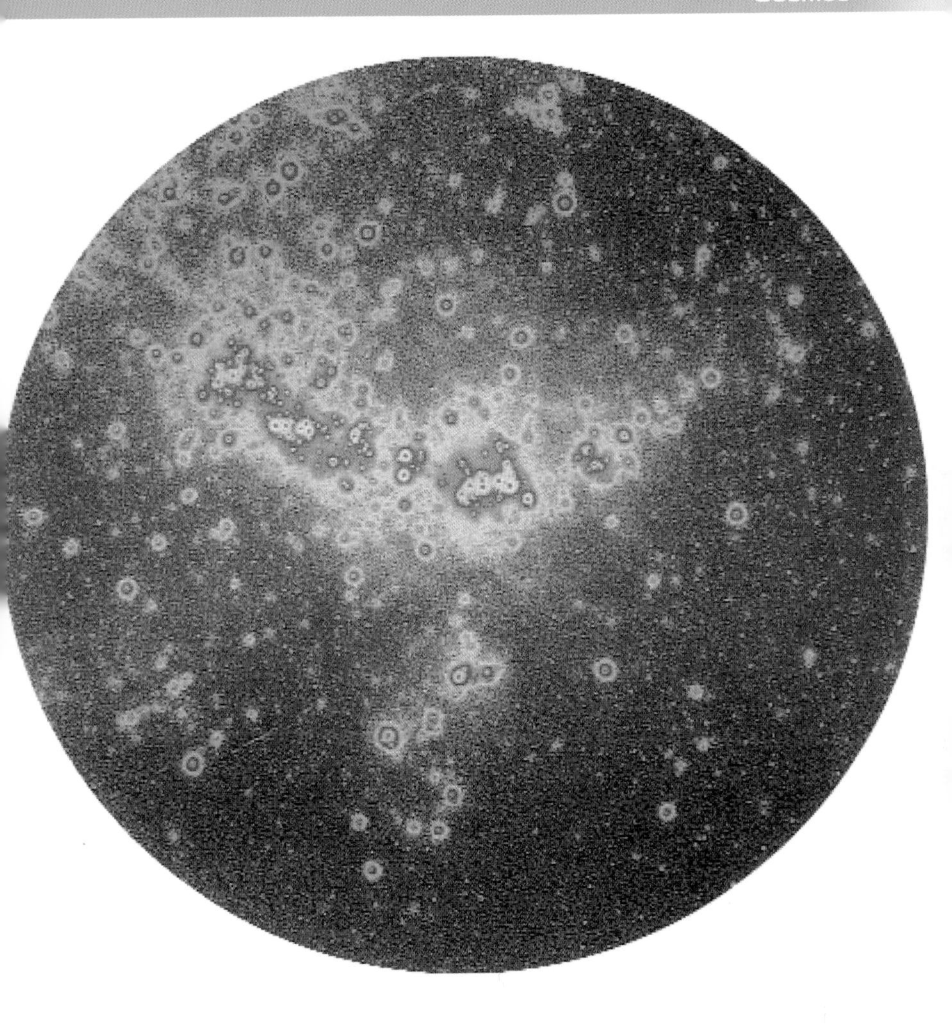

GLOBULAR CLUSTER 47 TUCANAE

This is a significant step in the story of our origins. For the first time, we have come close enough to home to give you a picture of an object within our own Galaxy. This is the globular cluster 47 Tucanae (also known as NGC 104), photographed by the AAT. It contains about a million stars in a spherically symmetrical ball, held together by gravity, and it lies in the bulge of our Galaxy (see pages 80 and 81, about 30,000 light years away from us. It is a typical globular cluster, one of about 150 known to be associated with our Galaxy. At the heart of a globular cluster, the stars are so densely packed together that there may be as many as a thousand stars within a cube of space three light years along each side. To put this in perspective, if such a cube were centred on our Sun there would be no other stars within it.

The way that globular clusters are distributed, forming a sphere around the Milky Way, shows that they formed when the Galaxy was young, before most of its material had settled down into the disk of the Milky Way. Spectroscopy shows that the stars in globular clusters contain very little in the way of heavy elements, confirming that they formed out of almost primordial material, and 47 Tucanae itself is one of the older globular clusters associated with our Galaxy, with an age of between 12 and 14 billion years. The oldest globular clusters are therefore among the first stellar populations that formed after the Big Bang, and were incorporated into what became our Galaxy (and other galaxies) when the Galaxy began to grow and attract material to itself by gravity. In a sense, the oldest globular clusters are older than the Galaxy itself.

AN OPEN STAR CLUSTER

The Sun and Solar System did not form as part of a globular cluster, but from a cloud of gas and dust which collapsed and fragmented to form a more irregular open cluster of stars. The open cluster in this image (NGC 6520, photographed by the AAT) happens to lie near to the position on the sky of a dust cloud like the one from which the Sun and a handful of other stars formed. The cloud looks like a hole in the profusion of stars of the Milky Way, through which we are looking out into the depths of space; in reality, it is a cloud of dark material blocking out the light from the stars behind it. The cloud has nothing to do with NGC 6520; they just happen to be close enough together on the sky to appear in the same photograph.

An open cluster may contain anything from a few dozen stars to a thousand or so stars, in a region a few light years across. They contain hot, young stars that have recently formed in the disk of our Galaxy, but because there are so few of them they are not held together in a permanent group by gravity. As the stars move around the Galaxy in their own independent orbits, they spread out, and the open cluster loses its identity. The stars that formed alongside our Sun some 4.5 billion years ago in an open cluster like this have long since gone their separate ways (the Sun has travelled right round the Galaxy about 200 times since then) and can no longer be identified.

THE MILKY WAY IN INFRARED

The 'fried egg' appearance of our own Milky Way Galaxy shows up clearly in the image overleaf, obtained by an instrument sensitive to infrared wavelengths of light, carried on the COBE satellite (see page 27. Because infrared radiation penetrates dust much more easily than visible light does, this instrument, the Diffuse Infrared Background Experiment (DIRBE), had a much clearer view of the stars in the disk and bulge of our Galaxy than the view available from telescopes operating in the part of the spectrum visible to our eyes. But because DIRBE operated in the near infrared, only just outside the visible band, most of the radiation it 'saw' did indeed come from stars, although these are not resolved individually and all we see is the overall pattern.

This image combines data from different parts of the sky obtained over a period of six months. It has been mapped onto a projection of the whole sky, as if the heavens were unwrapped and laid out flat; this is similar to the way in which the surface of the entire spherical Earth can be mapped onto a flat piece of paper using the Mercator projection. Like the Mercator projection, this map is distorted near the poles, at the top and bottom of the map – but in this case there is nothing much there to be distorted.

The middle of the picture is centred on the view towards the bulge of the Milky Way (the centre of our Galaxy), and the left and right edges of the picture should be imagined as wrapped round to join behind the back of your head, giving the view out towards the edge of the disk. But because most of the radiation detected by DIRBE comes from the much denser population of stars towards the galactic centre, and very little comes from the thin population of stars in the opposite direction, there is an illusion of viewing the Milky Way from the outside (compare this with the image of the edge-on spiral NGC 4945 shown on page 65). The image certainly gives a feel for how far away we are from the centre of the Galaxy. As a bonus, some of the globular clusters surrounding the Milky Way can also be seen in this picture.

THE CENTRE OF THE MILKY WAY

You can get some idea of why the infrared detector on the COBE satellite was needed to obtain the image on pages 80 and 81 from this view of part of the Milky Way in visible light, obtained using a wide-angle exposure on the Anglo-Australian Telescope. There are certainly plenty of stars to be seen; but the plane of the disk of our Galaxy is also full of dark clouds of gas and dust, which obscure the view towards the heart of the Milky Way – once again, it is worth comparing this image with the picture of NGC 4945 on page 65.

But although all of the dust in the plane of the Milky Way hinders astronomical observations of the galactic centre, we should not be too annoyed by its presence, since without it we would not be here. It is the dusty clouds in galaxies like our own Milky Way and NGC 4945 that are the birthplaces of stars and planets, including our Sun and Solar System.

THE CONE NEBULA

This is a stellar birthplace of our own Galaxy, the young star cluster NGC 2264. When a star forms from a contracting ball of gas, it gets hot in the middle and starts to glow. The heat comes from gravitational energy released by the collapse of the proto-star, and it produces a pressure which slows down the contraction of the ball of gas. But the amount of heat released is not enough to stop the proto-star collapsing, and it continues to shrink slowly and get hotter and hotter inside. When it gets hot enough, at a central temperature of about 1.5 million degrees C, nuclear reactions begin to take place in its centre, and these generate enough energy to stop the star from collapsing any more – at least, until the nuclear fuel runs out. A star like our Sun, burning nuclear fuel steadily and staying the same size, is said to be a member of the main sequence of stars. But the stars in NGC 2264 are only a few million years old, and are still contracting – they have not yet reached the main sequence where nuclear reactions begin to take place.

The striking dark streak in the bottom of the picture, a cloud of cool material silhouetted against the bright background, is known, for obvious reasons, as the Cone Nebula.

THE TARANTULA NEBULA

One of the most spectacular regions of star formation in our relatively near neighbourhood can be seen in this AAT image (overleaf) of the Tarantula Nebula, 160,000 light years away in the Large Magellanic Cloud (not far from the site of Supernova 1987A; see page 99. It gets its name because of a fancied resemblance to the spider; more prosaically, it is part of a system known as the 30 Doradus complex.

The Tarantula is about a thousand light years across – so big that, even at the distance of the LMC, it covers half a degree of arc on the sky (about the same as the Moon) and can be seen with the naked eye. Another famous nebula that can be seen with the naked eye is the Orion Nebula, only about 1,300 light years away in the constellation of the same name, within our own Galaxy. The Tarantula system is thirty times the size of the Orion Nebula, but a hundred times further away; if the two were swapped the Tarantula Nebula would not only be visible by day, but would cast shadows at night.

The whole complex contains about 500,000 times as much mass as our Sun, and will probably form a globular cluster made up of at least 100,000 stars. Much of this mass is now in the form of very hot, very young and very massive stars at the heart of the nebula – it is estimated that there are about twenty stars, each with a mass between 100 and 200 times the mass of our Sun, as well as a profusion of smaller stars. The energy output from all the stars in the centre of the nebula is 50 million times the energy output of the Sun. A great deal of this energy is in the form of ultraviolet radiation, which is absorbed by the nebula and makes it glow (not unlike the way in which a UV light at a disco makes a white shirt glow).

The Tarantula Nebula is also visible in the ultraviolet image of the LMC on page 73, near the point where the bar across the image bends upwards.

THE LAGOON NEBULA

Although much more modest in size than the Tarantula Nebula, the Lagoon nebula, shown here in an image obtained by the HST, is much closer to home, so it can be studied in detail. This system is very like the kind of stellar nursery in which our Solar System was born.

The Lagoon Nebula (also known as M8) lies 5,000 light years from Earth in the direction of the constellation Sagittarius. The light we see it by left the nebula about the time that the first stage of Stonehenge and the Pyramid of Giza were being built on Earth. The bright central region of the nebula (upper left in this image), called the Hourglass, is illuminated by the radiation from a hot central star. Together with other hot stars in the nebula, the energy output from this star is producing a strong stellar wind which is ripping apart the cool clouds of material around the stars.

Where the surfaces of the clouds are heated by the stellar wind, a blue mist of material is being driven off and blown away into space on the right-hand side of the picture. The difference in temperature between the hot surfaces of the clouds and their cold interiors, combined with the pressure of the stellar wind, has twisted some of the clouds into spiralling streamers, like interstellar tornadoes, each half a light year long.

The picture also shows a variety of smaller features within the nebula, including small dark blobs known as Bok globules. These are tiny clouds (by astronomical standards), each only about 8,000 times as big across as the distance from the Earth to the Sun, on the point of collapsing to form stars. Each globule contains somewhere between a tenth and ten or twenty times as much mass as our Sun.

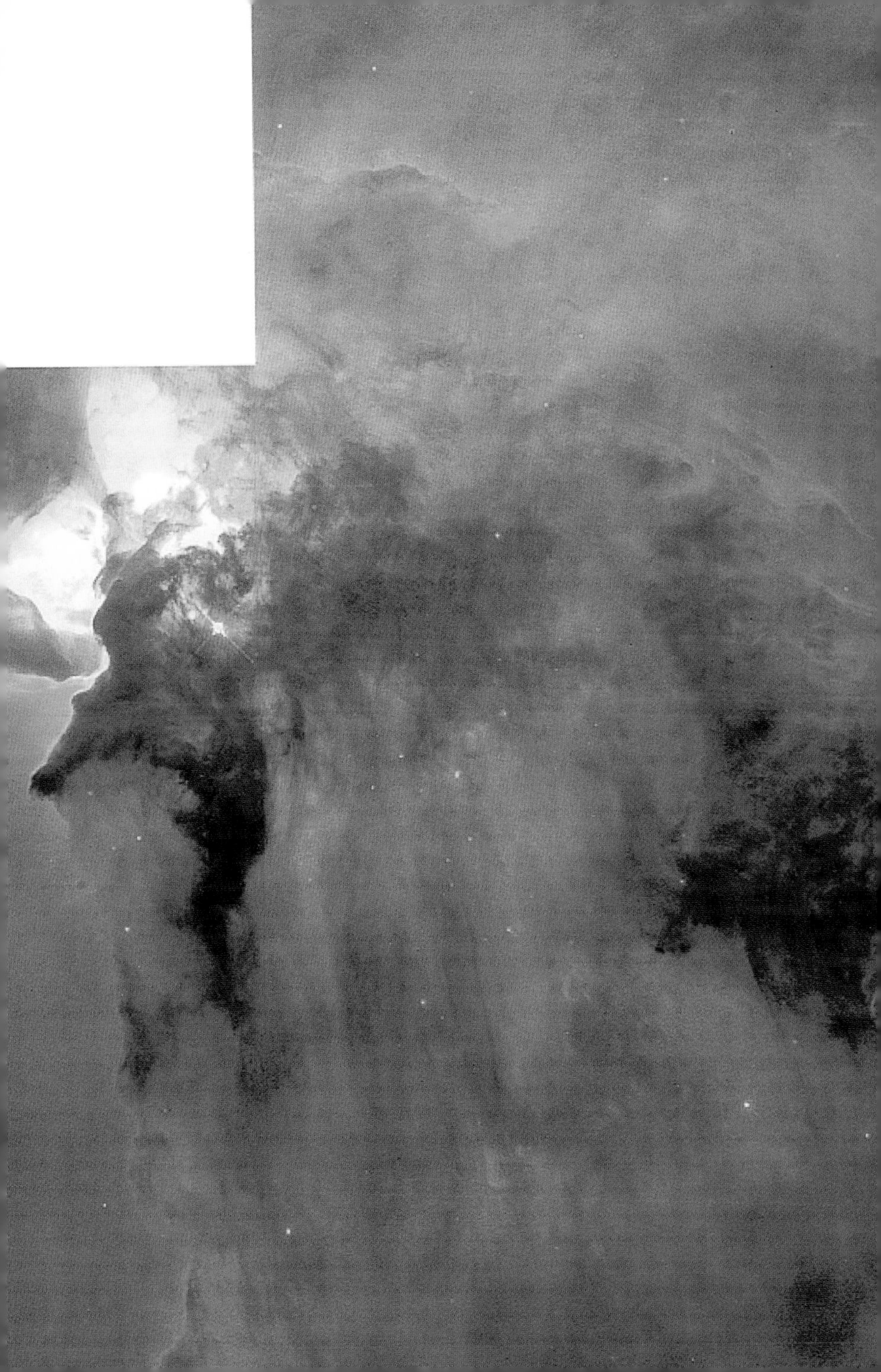

A STARBURST IN NGC 253

If you were still under any illusions that the Earth and the Solar System occupy any kind of special place in the Universe, this image should shatter those illusions once and for all. It is not part of the Milky Way, but the central region of a starburst galaxy (see also page 69 known as NGC 253, which lies 8 million light years from Earth, in the direction of (but far beyond!) the constellation Sculptor. This HST image shows a region about 1,000 light years across, in which a huge number of stars are forming simultaneously. Each bright white blob in this picture represents not a single star, but a stellar nursery like the Lagoon Nebula, in which many stars are forming.

Galaxies like these are shrouded in dust (which is what the new stars and planets form from), so a great deal of the light from the young stars is obscured. This radiation (largely blue and ultraviolet light from hot young stars) is absorbed by the dusty clouds, and re-radiated in the form of infrared radiation, so starburst galaxies show up very brightly in infrared images of the sky. Many starburst galaxies were discovered by the Infrared Astronomical Satellite (IRAS), which flew in space in the early 1980s. Starburst galaxies are often otherwise ordinary disk galaxies involved in collisions or tidal interactions with other galaxies, which have triggered the burst of star formation.

There are more than 100 billion stars in our Galaxy alone, and more than 50 billion galaxies in the visible Universe, each roughly the same sort of size as our Galaxy, and there are millions more stars being made in some of those galaxies all the time. Even if the odds against any particular one of those star systems containing a planet like Earth, with blue skies and running water, are very small, there are so many star systems out there that there must be millions of planets like the Earth somewhere in the Universe.

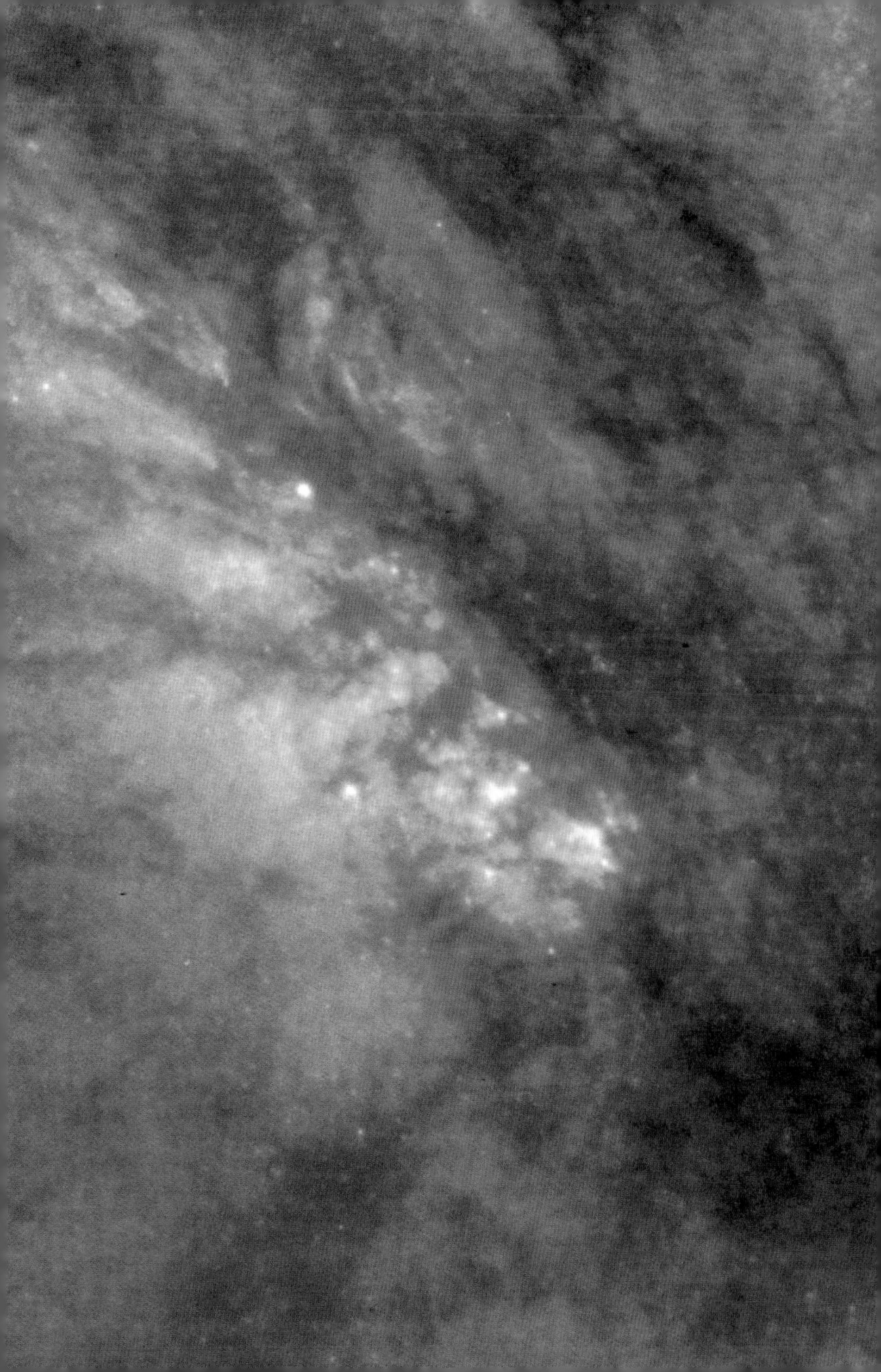

STARBIRTH IN M33

Even in ordinary galaxies which are not undergoing a starburst there are likely to be regions in which there is a great deal of star-forming activity. One of these regions, a nebula known as NGC 604, is pictured here in an image from the HST. NGC 604 lies in the outer regions of the disk of an ordinary spiral galaxy (very similar to the Milky Way) called M33. M33 is just 2.7 million light years away from us, in the direction of the constellation Triangulum.

There are at least 200 hot, young stars at the heart of the NGC 604, each of them with a mass between twenty-five to sixty times the mass of our Sun, plus (it is assumed) many smaller stars. The energy from these stars is absorbed by the gas in the nebula, which glows as the energy it has absorbed is re-radiated. This image strikingly reveals the three-dimensional structure of the nebula, with cavernous holes in the clouds made by the pressure of the energy being radiated by the stars inside it, pushing the material away into space. Eventually, the cloud will disperse and the stars will settle down as an open cluster (see page 77).

COMETARY GLOBULE CG4

Looking more like a creature from a science fiction horror movie than anything else, this is in fact a gas cloud known as a cometary globule, and given the prosaic catalogue number CG4. Cometary globules have nothing at all to do with comets, but get their name from the superficial resemblance to a comet seen in the night sky from Earth. The head of such a globule is larger than the entire Solar System, and the tail (only part of which is visible in the AAT picture of CG4) stretches for more than 200 billion km – about 100,000 light minutes, or a fifth of a light year.

Cometary globules are a by-product of starbirth, in nebulas like NGC 604 (see page 95). They form when a region of hot gas being blown out from the vicinity of a hot young star (or stars) collides with cooler material in space. In this case, the collision between the hot, glowing material of the cometary globule and cold, invisible gas has given the head of the globule the appearance of a mouth about to devour a galaxy. But this is simply a trick of perspective: the edge-on disk galaxy to the left of the picture is actually millions of light years away, far outside our own Galaxy, while the cometary globule is part of the Milky Way.

LIGHT ECHOES ROUND SUPERNOVA 1987A

From starbirth to stardeath. The elements from which the Earth and everything on it, including the material of your own body, are made and were manufactured inside stars which exploded at the ends of their lives and scattered the material into space, where it formed the raw material for stars like the Sun and planets like the Earth. The most violent of these stellar explosions are known as Type II supernovas. They occur when a star more than ten times as massive as our Sun has exhausted all of its nuclear fuel, and can no longer produce the energy needed to hold itself up against the inward pull of gravity. It is as if the floor were pulled from under the star, and the whole core of the star suddenly collapses into a ball only a few kilometres across (perhaps even into a black hole). This releases a blast of gravitational energy so powerful that in a few seconds the star releases ten times as much energy as the Sun will release in 10 billion years of quiet nuclear burning. This blasts the outer layers of the star away into space, at speeds of up to 10,000 km per second.

The most recent nearby supernova of this kind was seen in the Large Magellanic Cloud in 1987, and is known as Supernova 1987A. The supernova occurred in the 30 Doradus complex, just below the Tarantula Nebula (see pages 88 and 89). Seven years later, the HST took this picture of the region where the supernova occurred. The two large glowing rings of material lie in front of and behind the site of the supernova itself; it is thought that they are part of a spherical shell of gas blasted out in the explosion and expanding away from where it occurred. The two rings are being illuminated by radiation from a tiny neutron star that was a companion of the supernova before it exploded. Beams of radiation from near the poles of the spinning neutron star are sweeping round on either side like two lighthouse beams; although

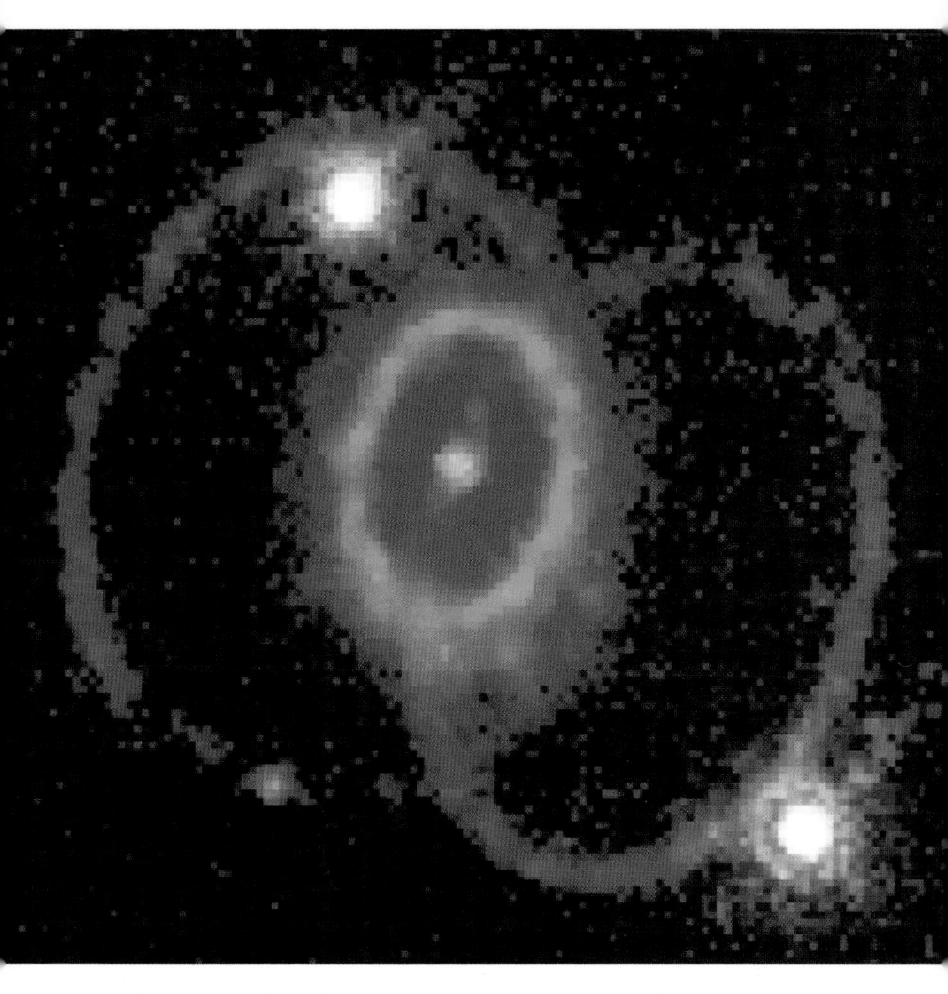

the beams are invisible, we can see their trace where they sweep across the gas from the supernova and energise it enough to make it glow.

The two white dots in the image are foreground stars in our own Galaxy; the inner bright ring marks a second shell of hot material expanding away more slowly from the site of the explosion.

SUPERNOVA 1987A BEFORE AND AFTER

This pair of AAT photographs gives some indication of just how bright a supernova is. The picture at the top of the page is a routine photograph of part of the Large Magellanic Cloud, taken before the supernova seen in February 1987 occurred. The image below is a picture of the same part of the LMC taken soon after Supernova 1987A was discovered, but when the exploding star had already just started to fade from its brightest glory. The arrow in the top part of the picture marks the star that exploded – a seemingly ordinary large blue star catalogued as Sanduleak -69° 202.

At its brightest, for several days a supernova like this will shine as brightly as an entire galaxy of a hundred billion stars put together.

THE CRAB NEBULA

A supernova even closer to home than Supernova 1987A was seen in our own Galaxy in AD 1054, before the invention of the telescope. It was observed by Chinese astronomers with the naked eye, and was so bright that it was visible in daylight for 23 days. The expanding cloud of material from that explosion is known as the Crab Nebula, and the material in the cloud is still moving outwards at a speed of about 1,500 kilometres per second. The nebula lies 7,000 light years away, in the constellation Taurus. Earlier, back in the 20th century, astronomers were puzzled when they discovered from studying photographs of the Crab Nebula (overleaf inset) that it must have been expanding at the same steady speed observed today for nine centuries – they had expected that the cloud would slow down as it moved away into space from the site of the supernova explosion. But the discovery of a pulsar in the heart of the Crab Nebula in 1967 explained what was going on. The Crab Pulsar is the remnant of the star that exploded, a cosmic cinder in the form of a neutron star in which about the same amount of mass as there is in the Sun is packed into a ball just 10 km across. The ball is spinning once every 0.033 seconds (that is, 30 times every second), and as it spins it is flicking around a beam of radio noise, like a superfast celestial lighthouse.

The 'radio lighthouse' is what we detect on Earth, and what tells us the pulsar is there. But the radio noise actually comes from charged particles (mainly electrons) which are being whirled around in the grip of the magnetic field of the neutron star, and are themselves being flung out at about the speed of light to collide with the gas of the nebula. Changing the analogy, it is like a super-powerful cosmic lawn sprinkler (a pair of similar sprinklers is responsible for the double rings associated with the remains of Supernova 1987A; see page 99). It is the energy from the pulsar that keeps pushing the material in the Crab Nebula outwards at a steady rate – the spinning neutron star stores so much energy (like a huge flywheel) that its measured slow-down, 300 billionths of a second each day, is exactly right to account for the entire energy output of the nebula, which is now 10 light years across.

When the HST turned its Wide Field Planetary Camera (WF/PC2) on to the central region of the Crab Nebula, it found even more direct evidence of the influence of the pulsar. In this image, the pulsar itself can be seen as the left-hand in the pair near the centre of the picture. The pulsar is surrounded by a complex mixture of knots and wisps in the gas of the Nebula, and you can clearly see a pattern of ripples, like the ripples made by a stone dropped in a pond, around the pulsar. Images like this taken in a sequence over a span of several months show that these ripples are moving outwards from the pulsar at half the speed of light, pushed by the intense beam of particles and radiation from its 'lighthouse'.

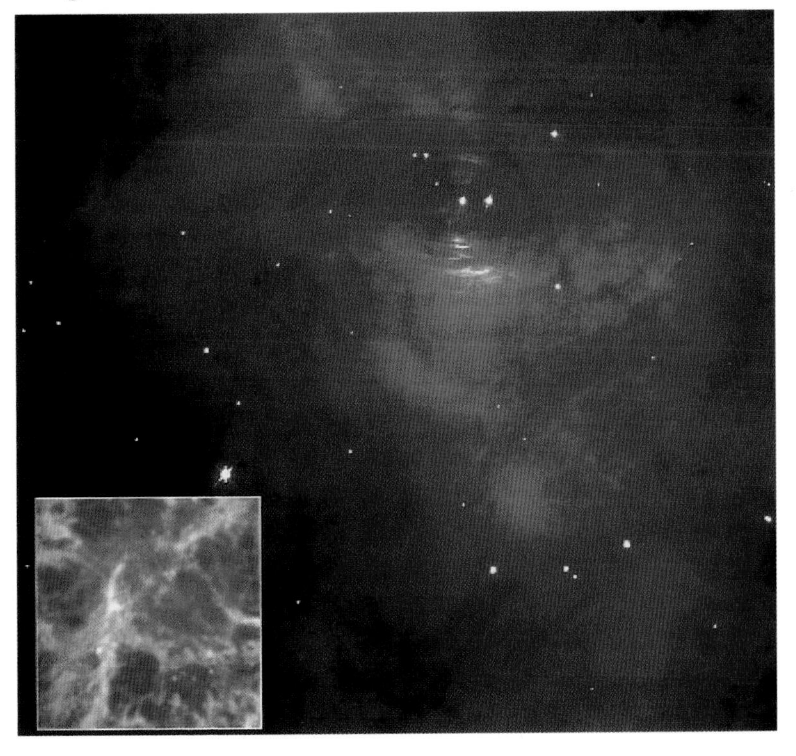

SUPERNOVA REMNANTS

This image shows two supernova remnants. Although they are superimposed on one another in this picture, this is simply because they happen to lie along the same line of sight. In fact, there is three times as much distance between the two remnants as there is between us and the nearer remnant. The smaller object, on the top right of the picture, is actually much further away along the line of sight. It is called the Puppis SNR, and is about 6,000 light years from Earth. Most of the image is filled with the much closer Vela SNR, which is only about 1,500 light years away, and has a diameter of about 230 light years. The light by which we see the Vela SNR today left it at about the time that the last vestiges of the Roman Empire in Italy were being overrun by invaders from the north. It took the remnant about 11,000 years to expand to this size from the supernova explosion in which it was born, so the supernova might have been seen by our ancestors around 9000 BC, about the time that agriculture was invented.

The image comes from X-ray observations made by the satellite ROSAT, launched in 1990. Although the two brightest parts of the Vela SNR can also be seen in optical light by ground-based telescopes, the X-ray observations were the first that showed the overall spherical structure of the remnant.

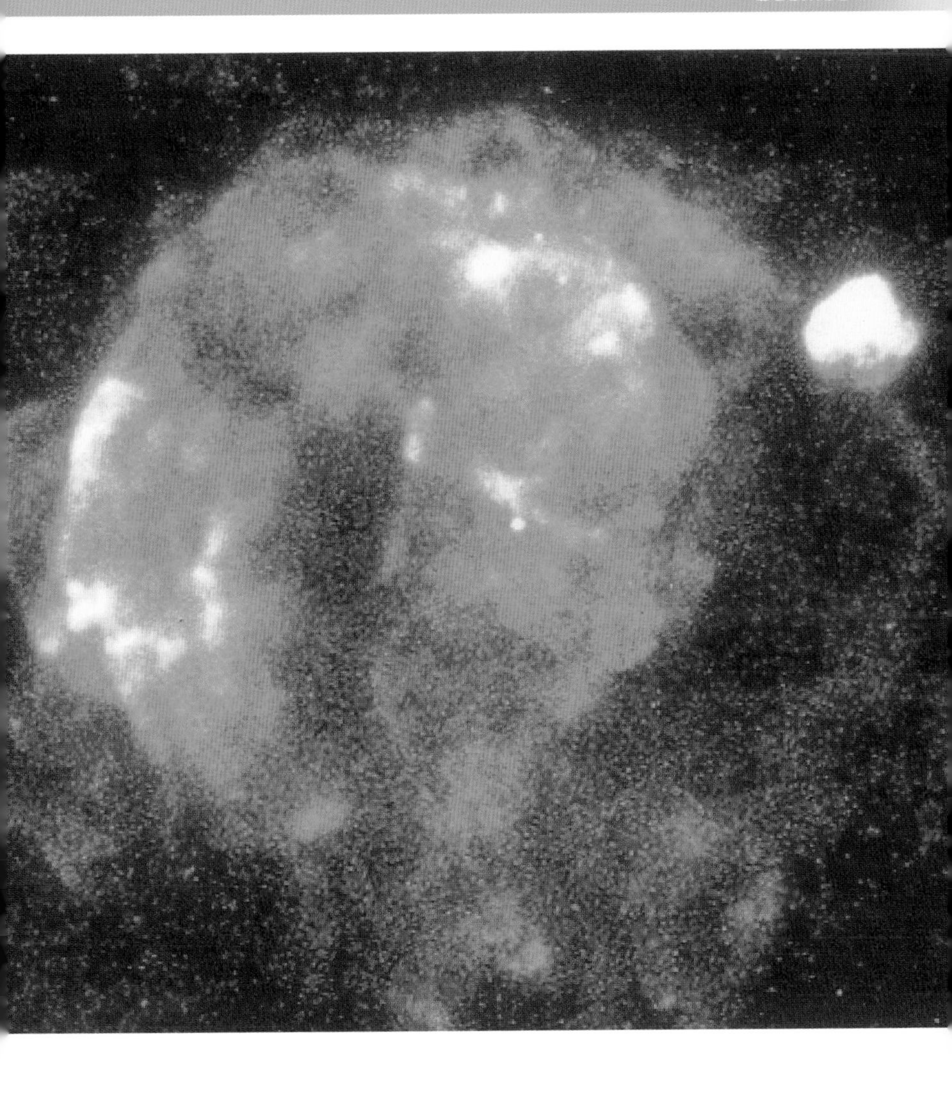

JUPITER AND THREE MOONS

The Sun and its family of planets formed together when a clump of gas and dust like the Bok globules in the image on page 91 collapsed in the wake of a supernova explosion which sent a blast wave rippling through the interstellar medium. Even though the cloud from which the Solar System formed was laced with heavier elements from previous stellar outbursts, the cloud still contained a mixture of 99.9 per cent hydrogen and helium (left over from the Big Bang) and only 0.1 per cent for everything else put together. In terms of the number of atoms around in the Solar System, sulphur is the tenth most common substance. For every atom of sulphur, there is 1 atom of iron, 2 atoms each of magnesium and neon, 3 atoms of silicon, 4 atoms of nitrogen, 20 atoms of carbon, 30 atoms of oxygen, 3,000 atoms of helium and 50,000 atoms of hydrogen. The Sun contains 99.86 per cent of the mass of the Solar System, and two-thirds of the remaining mass is concentrated in the giant planet Jupiter, pictured overleaf in a photograph taken by the probe Voyager 1 in 1979.

Jupiter is five times further from the Sun than we are, and has 318 times as much mass as the Earth (0.1 per cent of the mass of the Sun). It is more than twice as big as all the other planets in the Solar System put together. The spacecraft was 28.4 million km from Jupiter when it obtained this image, which shows the Great Red Spot and three of Jupiter's moons. Io is silhouetted as a brown-yellow disk against the bulk of Jupiter, while Callisto looks like a blob in the northern (left) hemisphere of the planet. Europa is to the right of Jupiter in this image.

Counting the planets inwards from outside the Solar System, after passing through the realm of the comets a visitor from another star would encounter first Pluto, a small icy world far from the

Sun, then the four gas giants Neptune, Uranus, Saturn and Jupiter, then a belt of rocky debris (the asteroid belt) and finally the four small, rocky planets Mars, Earth, Venus and, closest of all to the Sun, Mercury.

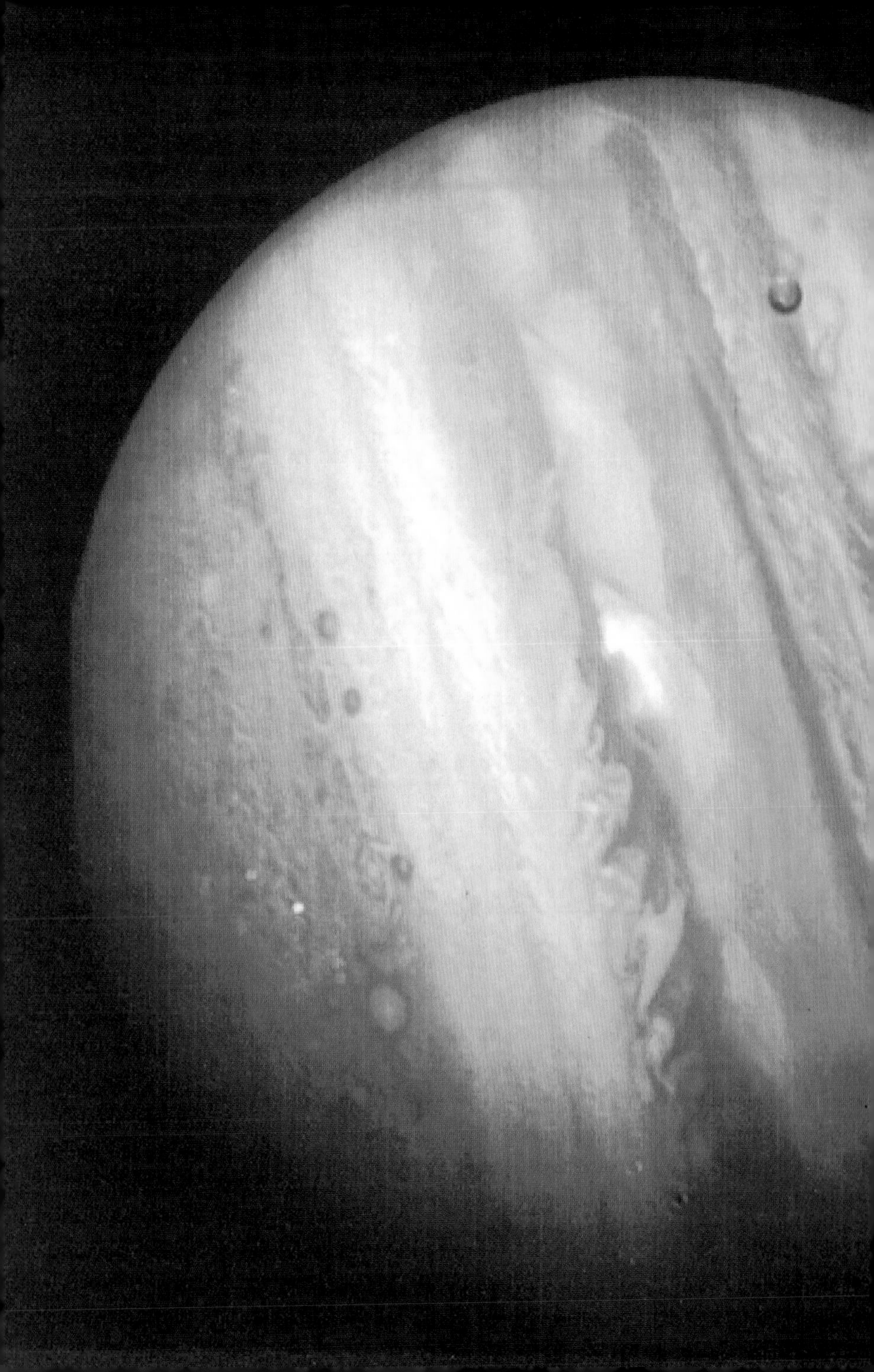

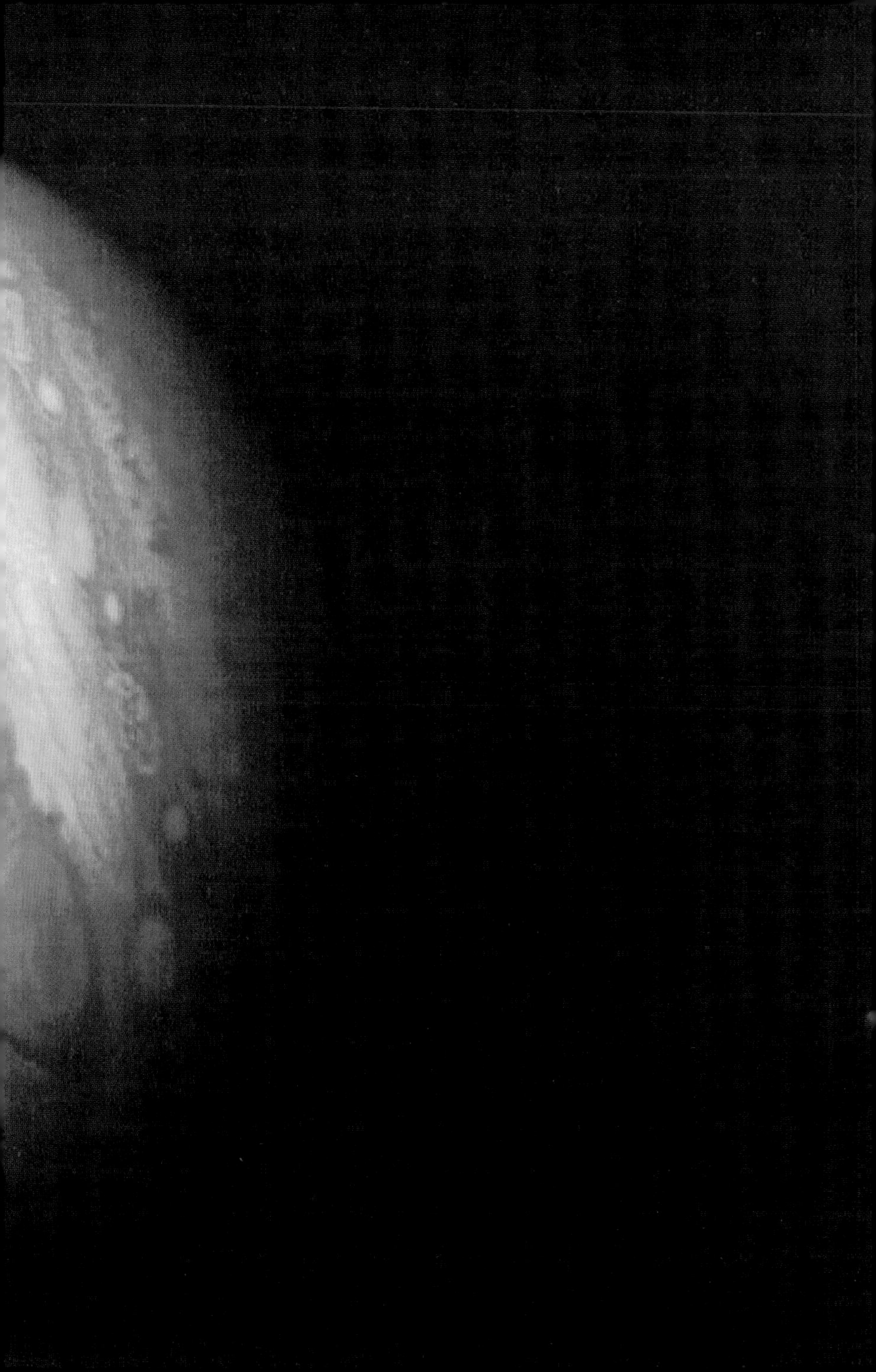

IO

Jupiter's moon Io is pictured here in an image obtained by the Galileo space probe in June 1996. Io is the innermost of the four large moons of Jupiter discovered by the astronomer Galileo early in the seventeenth century. It orbits only 422,000 km from the planet, and is locked in a gravitational embrace so that it always keeps the same face towards Jupiter (just as our Moon always keeps the same face towards the Earth). The diameter of Io is 3,630 km, and it has a mass one-fifth greater than that of our Moon. The strong tidal forces produced by Jupiter repeatedly squeeze and stretch the moon, heating its interior and making it the most volcanically active object in the Solar System. The yellowish-brown colour of the surface is a result of this activity, which spews sulphurous material out from within the moon; some of these sulphurous equivalents of lava flows stretch for 200 km from the volcanoes which gave them birth.

SATURN

Although it is smaller than Jupiter (its mass is only ninety-five times that of the Earth) and further out from the Sun (roughly twice as far), Saturn is one of the most intriguing and beautiful objects in the Solar System because of its prominent system of rings. This view of Saturn as a crescent, with its shadow eclipsing part of the ring system, was obtained from Voyager 1 in November 1980, four days after it had passed Saturn on its way out of the Solar System, looking back towards the planet. Just as the planet eclipses part of the rings, so the rings cast a shadow on part of the planet. The rings are not solid, but are made up of countless pieces of ice and rock, each orbiting the planet in its own trajectory. As well as the rings, Saturn has more than twenty moons. Like Jupiter, which has least 16 moons, in some ways it resembles a 'solar system' in miniature. It is likely that the planets themselves formed from a similar but much larger ring system around the young Sun, with the pieces of material in the rings colliding and sticking together, building up to make the planets.

The outermost of the gas giants, Uranus and Neptune, resemble Saturn, but without the prominent rings. As the name implies, they are largely composed of gas, chiefly hydrogen, much of which is locked up in compounds such as methane and ammonia.

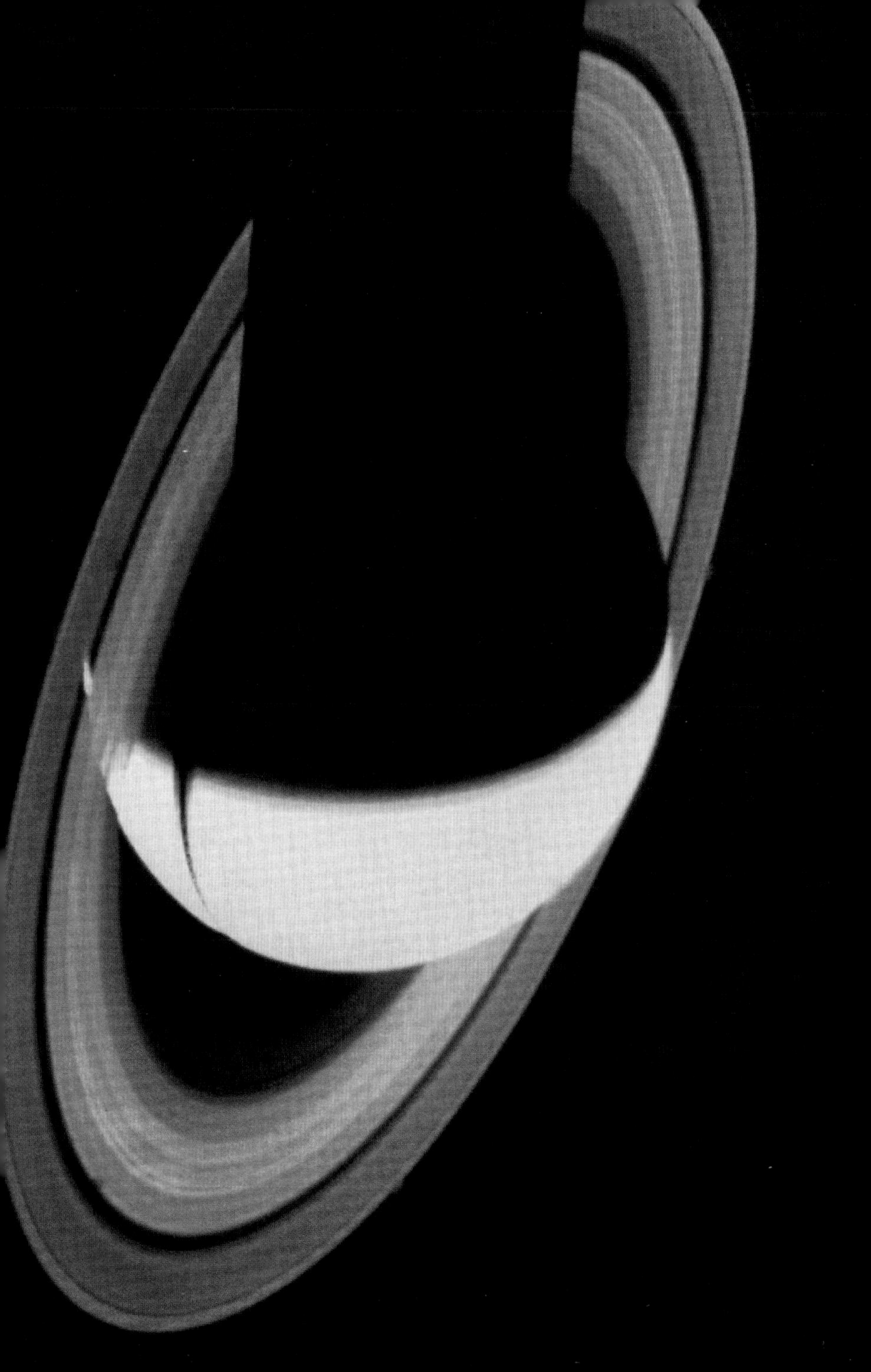

MARS

The first of the small, rocky planets that our visitor from another star would encounter on a journey towards the centre of the Solar System is Mars, the red planet. It isn't really quite as red as this, but the colour has been enhanced in this picture, obtained by the Viking Orbiter mission, to bring out the detail.

Mars has a mass only a little more than one-tenth of that of the Earth, and a diameter roughly half that of the Earth. It orbits the Sun once every 686.98 of our days, at an average distance of one and a half times further from the Sun than we are. It has a thin atmosphere of carbon dioxide, and turns on its axis once every 24 hours, 37 minutes and 23 seconds, giving it a day about the same length as ours. This is a coincidence.

In terms of origins, the most important thing to notice about Mars is the battered state of its surface, smothered in impact craters. Because the atmosphere of Mars is thin, there has been much less weathering of the surface than occurs on Earth. And because there is no life on Mars, the surface features have not been obliterated by vegetation. What we see here is evidence, in the form of the record in the rocks, of the last great phase of planet building, when rocks rained down on Mars about 4 billion years ago, as it swept up the last of the debris in its orbit.

VENUS

The surface of Venus is very different from that of Mars. From a comparison between the number of craters on Venus and the number of craters seen on the surfaces of the Moon (pages 136 and 137) and Mercury (page 121), astronomers infer that the whole surface of Venus was turned over some 600 million years ago, in a great cataclysm in which so much lava flowed out from its interior through cracks in its crust that the entire planet was resurfaced with new rock. All the craters we see today on the surface of Venus were formed by impacts within the past 600 million years; this discovery has some bearing on the understanding of our own origins (see page 139).

Venus has a very dense carbon dioxide atmosphere, and is completely shrouded with clouds rich in sulphuric acid, so no information about its surface was available until astronomers developed techniques to map the planet by radar. The image overleaf is mainly a result of radar mapping by the space probe Magellan, which went into orbit around Venus and charted 98 per cent of its surface.

The gaps have been filled in using data from earlier missions, both Soviet and American, with some data coming from Earth-based radar observations using the Arecibo radio telescope in Puerto Rico.

The colours used to produce this image are based on the actual colours at the surface of Venus seen by the Soviet probes Venera 13 and Venera 14, which landed on the planet and sent back data briefly before being simultaneously cooked, corroded and crushed by the enormous pressure at the surface – ninety times the atmospheric pressure at sea level on Earth.

The planet's highest mountain range, Maxwell Montes, is the bright feature just below the middle of this image; it rises 11 km above its surroundings. The image also shows lava flows, impact craters, ridges and other structures.

Venus is the second planet out from the Sun. It has 82 per cent as much mass as the Earth, and orbits the Sun once every 225 days at, on average, 72 per cent of our distance from the Sun. It rotates very slowly, once every 243 of our days. Because of a combination of its proximity to the Sun and the strong greenhouse effect of its thick carbon dioxide atmosphere, the surface temperature of Venus is above 450 degrees C. The surface is a searing, lifeless desert, scoured by strong winds and showers of acid rain.

MERCURY

Mercury is the innermost planet of the Solar System, orbiting the Sun at only 39 per cent of the distance from the Earth to the Sun, and taking only 87.97 of our days to complete each orbit. It turns on its own axis once every 58.64 of our days, so that three 'days' on Mercury last for two of the planet's 'years'. Its mass is only 5 per cent of that of the Earth, and its diameter is 4,880 km, making it intermediate in size between the Moon and Mars. It has no atmosphere at all, so there has never been any weathering of its surface. And, unlike Venus, its surface has never been overturned in a cataclysmic upheaval. So the surface of Mercury carries a reminder of every blow from space that has ever struck it, and provides the best record we have of just how intense the bombardment of the inner planets has been. This record is clearly shown in the image, a mosaic of pictures sent back by the probe Mariner 10, which flew past Mercury in 1974. The image has been highlighted in false colour to show the details.

The most spectacular impact feature on Mercury is the Caloris Basin, about 1,300 km across and surrounded by a ring of mountains 2 km high, created in the impact. The basin is big enough to contain the British Isles. The evidence of extensive cratering right across the inner part of the Solar System, from Mars to Mercury, shows that the bombardment which occurred 4 billion years ago was not restricted to just one planet, but happened right across this region as the rocky planets formed by sweeping up cosmic debris. The cratering of Venus over the past 600 million years, though, shows that there are still traces of that debris around in our part of the Solar System, and that from time to time such rocks from space still strike the inner planets – including the Earth (see pages 142 and 143).

THE SUN

Our Sun, which sits at the centre of the Solar System, is an ordinary star, roughly halfway through its lifetime on the main sequence. It only looks big and bright to us, compared with other stars, because it is so close – the Sun is 150 million km away, but the next nearest star is more than 4 light years away. The Sun is a ball of hot gas (roughly three-quarters hydrogen and one-quarter helium) with 330,000 times as much mass as the Earth and a diameter 109 times the diameter of the Earth. This gives it an overall density of a third of the Earth's density, only 1.4 times the density of water. But that average disguises the fact that the outer layers of the Sun are very tenuous, while the innermost core is very dense.

At the heart of the Sun, its material is packed together so tightly that it has 160 times the density of water (twelve times the density of lead). But instead of being made of atoms, this core material is made of nuclei of hydrogen and helium, atomic kernels stripped of their electrons, and even at these densities it behaves like a gas. The density drops off slightly over the inner 1.5 per cent of the Sun (15,000 times the volume of the Earth), which actually contains half of its total mass (roughly 150,000 times the mass of the Earth). The temperature at the centre of this core is about 15 million degrees C, and the pressure is 300 billion times the atmospheric pressure at the surface of the Earth.

Above this core, the density drops rapidly, to be the same as water halfway to the surface of the Sun, and as thin as the air we breathe two-thirds of the way to the surface. In the top 10 per cent of the Sun, the density is less than 1 per cent of the density of water. At the visible surface of the Sun, the temperature is only 6,000 degrees C. But as this image shows, the Sun extends into space beyond the visible surface, through a tenuous layer known as the chromosphere into the corona, which extends for millions of kilometres into space, and blends into the so-called solar wind of particles that stream outwards from the Sun and (among other things) cause the auroras here on Earth.

This image is of the Sun as you will never see it, observed in 1996 by detectors on board the SOHO satellite, sensitive to extreme ultraviolet radiation. The green colour has been chosen arbitrarily to bring out the detail, which includes flaring activity on the surface of the Sun and a very clear system of arching loops, called prominences, on the left-hand side of the picture. The Earth would fit comfortably under one of these arches, which are temporary features linked to the activity of the Sun's magnetic field.

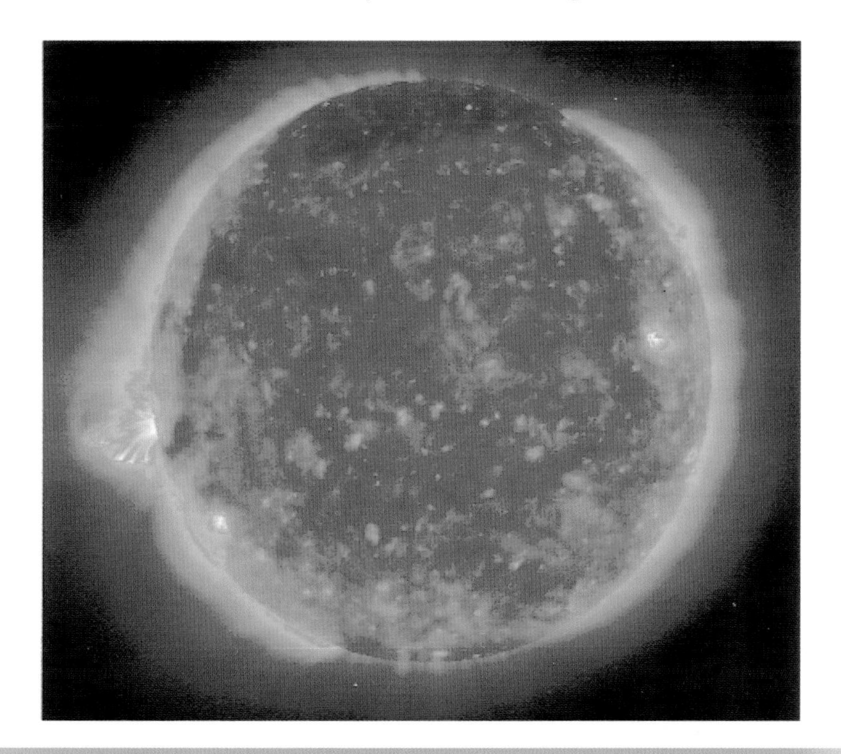

HALLEY'S COMET

The image most of us have of a comet is like the photogenic visitor from space pictured on page 31. But what causes this heavenly display? In 1986, the space probe Giotto carried out a close encounter with Halley's Comet, and sent back this picture of the lump of material at its head. A comet is, in fact, a lump of icy material and dust (a 'dirty snowball') which spends most of its life in the outer reaches of the Solar System, where it is undetectable. It is only when a comet is disturbed into an orbit that brings it into the inner Solar System, where it is heated by the rays of the Sun, that material begins to boil off from its surface (as you see happening at the bottom left of the picture overleaf) and create the spectacular tail that gives the characteristic appearance of a comet seen from Earth.

There are thought to be billions of these cometary nuclei, as they are called, in a cloud orbiting the Sun in leisurely fashion literally halfway to the nearest star, far beyond the orbit of Pluto. They are bits of primordial material left over from the origin of the Solar System. The mass of all these comets put together adds up to about a hundred times the mass of the Earth. When, occasionally, one or more of these objects gets disturbed (perhaps by the gravity of a passing star), and falls into the inner Solar System, some (like Halley's Comet) are captured by the gravity of Jupiter into an orbit which brings them looping past the Sun repeatedly. Halley's Comet itself has an orbit 76 years long, taking it out beyond the orbit of Neptune, and in to within the orbit of Venus.

The nucleus of Halley's Comet is shaped like a lumpy potato, about 16 km long and 8 km wide, similar to the size of the island of Manhattan. About 80 per cent of its mass is in the form of water ice, and the rest is made up of lumps of rock embedded in the ice.

The whole thing is covered in a black layer of carbon dust (soot), and has a mass of 300 billion tonnes. Comets in orbits like that of Halley's Comet cross the orbit of the Earth, so if the Earth is in the right (or wrong!) part of its orbit at the right time, it can get stuck by such lumps of cosmic debris. It is almost certain that the catastrophe that killed the dinosaurs and many other forms of life on Earth 65 million years ago was due to an impact of this kind.

ASTEROID IDA AND ITS MOON

Comets are not the only kinds of debris still floating around the Solar System, left over from the material out of which the planets were made. Very many lumps of rocky material, parts of a proto-planet that failed to form, orbit in a band known as the asteroid belt (like the rings of Saturn on a very large scale) between the orbits of Jupiter and Mars. The reason why they failed to form a planet is the disturbing influence of Jupiter's gravitational pull. More than 5,000 members of this asteroid belt have been identified and catalogued. There are probably half a million of them big enough to be seen using the 200-inch (5-metre) telescope at Mount Palomar (if anyone could be bothered to look for them), and many millions more with sizes of a few hundred metres.

The image overleaf shows a typical member of the asteroid belt, known as 243 Ida, photographed by the space probe Galileo in August 1993 on its way to Jupiter (the number means that Ida was the 243rd asteroid to be identified). This particular asteroid is about 58 km long and 21 km wide. The Galileo images also revealed, for the first time, that Ida has a tiny moon, dubbed Dactyl, visible at the top of this picture. Dactyl is only 1.6 km long and 1.2 km wide, and orbits Ida at a distance of 90 km. By measuring the orbit of Dactyl around Ida, astronomers can work out the mass of the asteroid; Ida has a mass of about 70 thousand billion tonnes.

The cameras on board Galileo were sensitive to infrared light, and to human eyes the asteroid would appear a dull grey. The colours in this image show details in the surface that would be missed by unaided human eyes, such as the bright bluish areas around some of the craters, which show a different amount of iron in these regions.

The orbits of the asteroids are still being perturbed by the gravity of Jupiter, so from time to time a member of the asteroid belt is disturbed into an orbit which takes it closer to the Sun. Some of these asteroids go so close to the Sun that they cross the orbit of the Earth, and they will stay in such an orbit until they hit something. Several such 'Earth-crossing' asteroids have been discovered, and there are certainly more that are too faint to be seen.

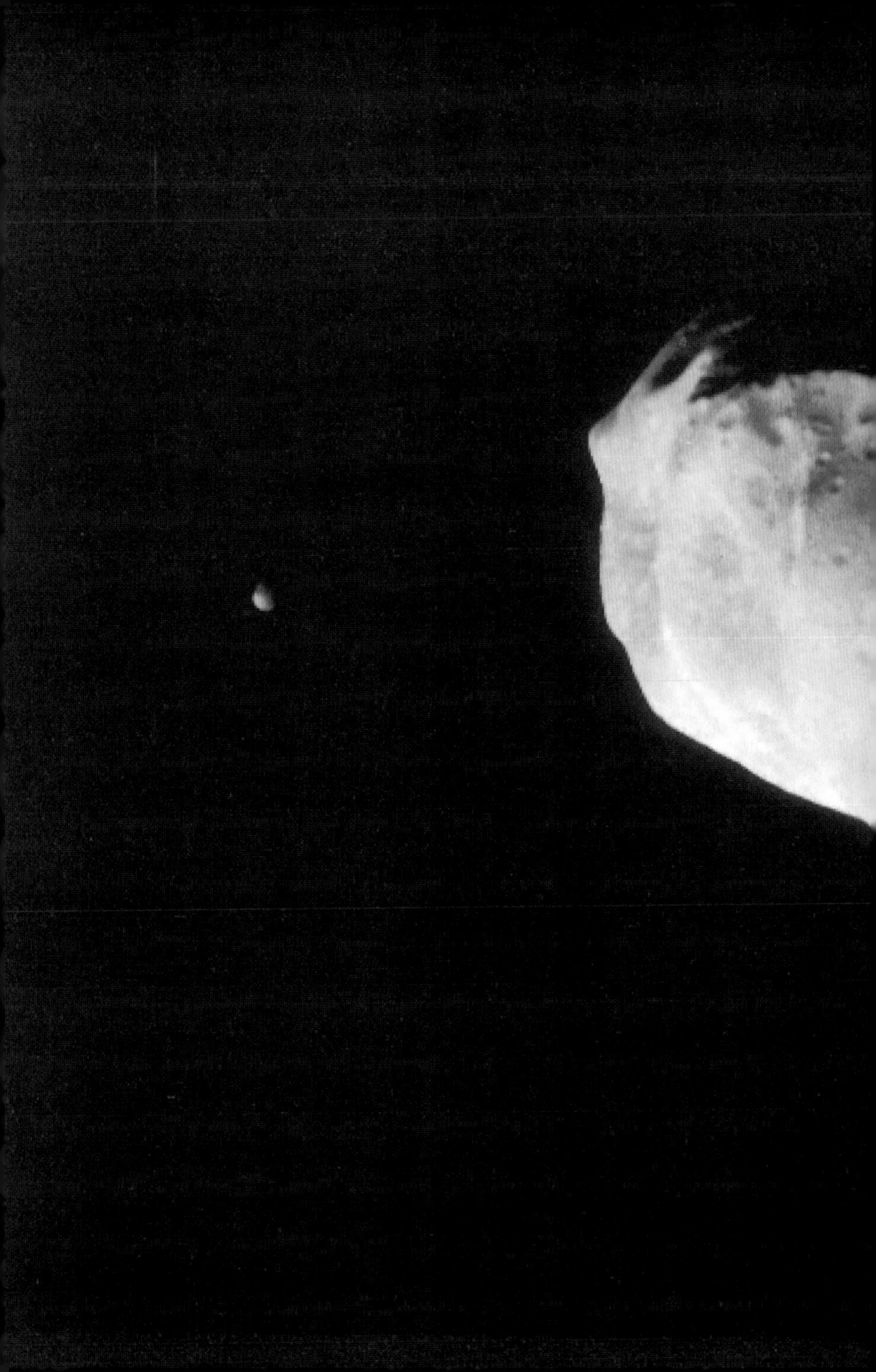

THE EARTH AND THE MOON

We have saved the best for last. This is our home in space, the Earth and the Moon photographed by the Galileo space probe in December 1992, looking back to home on its way to Jupiter. The picture was taken from a distance of 6.2 million km; the bright Earth reflects three times as much sunlight as the Moon does. Antarctica is just visible through the clouds on Earth, but the Moon has an unfamiliar appearance because we are looking at the side that is always turned away from the Earth. The shadowy indentation that can just be discerned in the surface of the Moon near to the boundary between its dark and sunlit sides (the line of dawn on the Moon) is the Aitken Basin, at the lunar South Pole. This is one of the largest and oldest impact features on the Moon. It is 13 km deep and 2,500 km across, and was created by the glancing impact of an asteroid 200 km across.

THE MOON

The battered face of the Moon is shown in detail in this false-colour image (overleaf) obtained by the Galileo space probe in December 1992. The part of the Moon visible from Earth is on the left-hand side of this picture. Bright, pinkish areas are the highland material, such as the mountains around the oval Crisium impact basin, a lava-filled crater at the bottom left of the picture. The solidified lava flows are coloured in shades from blue to orange. To the left of Crisium, the Mare Tranquillitatis shows up dark blue, because the lava there is particularly rich in titanium. Thin layers of material spread by relatively recent impacts show up light blue; the youngest craters have bright blue rays extending out from them.

Because the Moon is airless, there has been no weathering; and because it is not geologically active, the surface has not been overturned like the surface of Venus (see pages 118 and 119). What we see on the surface of the Moon today is a record of the battering it has received over the past 4 billion years or so. We know that this was not a unique battering caused by the way the Moon formed in orbit around the Earth, because similar craters are seen on the surfaces of Mercury, Venus and Mars. So there is no doubt that the Earth has received a similar pounding down the aeons.

Most of the battering occurred about 4 billion years ago, in the last stages of the formation of the Moon and the inner planets of the Solar System. The Tranquillitatis lava flow, for example, is 3.8 billion years old, and it is among the youngest material on the surface of the Moon. But there are many younger craters scarring the surface of such ancient lunar lava flows. If you were to draw a circle 100 km in diameter at random anywhere on the surface of the Moon you would find 500 craters at least a kilometre in diameter, all younger than 600 million years. From this evidence, and from counts of the numbers of craters on Mercury, Venus and Mars, astronomers calculate that an object bigger than 1 km across hits the Earth (which is a much bigger target than the Moon) once every 200,000 years or so, releasing the energy equivalent of the explosion of a 20,000 megatonne nuclear bomb (400 times more powerful than any bomb ever exploded on Earth), and producing a crater 20 km across. An object big enough to make a crater 100 km across strikes our planet roughly every 50 million years.

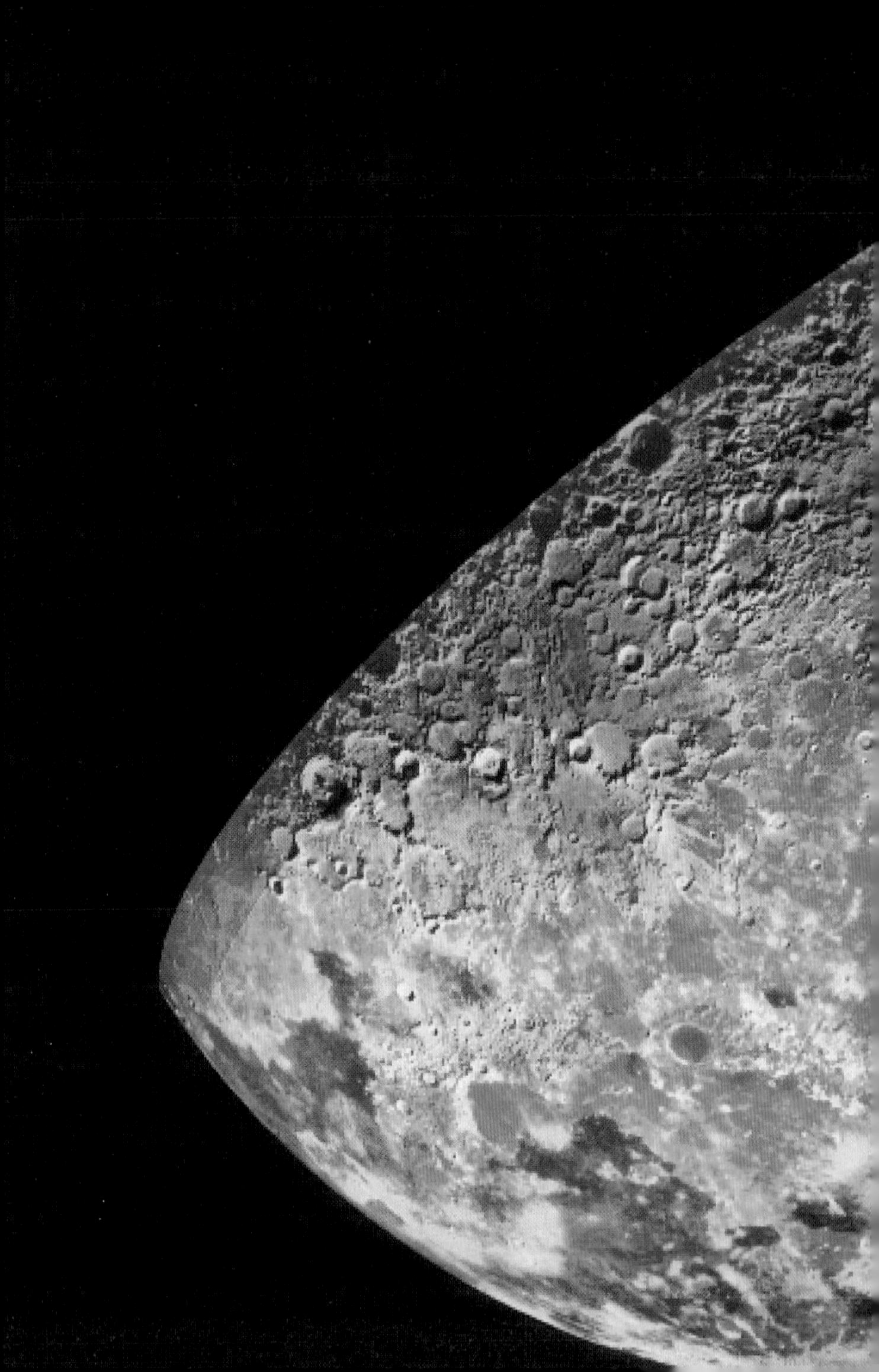

THE EARTH

It is hard to believe that the tranquil Earth, floating peacefully in space, is subject to a rain of cosmic missiles, and has been battered by impacts as much as the surface of the Moon or any of the other inner planets of the Solar System. The evidence is not obvious because even over the third of Earth that is not covered by water, wind and weather have worn away the craters from the impacts; and although our planet has not been subjected to the same kind of cataclysmic upheaval that occurred on Venus 600 million years ago, the surface layer of the Earth is constantly being recycled, spreading out from ocean ridges and being pushed back down into the interior of the planet in deep trenches along the edges of some continents. As a result, none of the present-day sea floor is more than 200 million years old, and even the continents are not as old as Mare Tranquillitatis (see pages 136 and 137). In addition, most of the impact sites that are still present on the surface of the Earth today are covered by vegetation, and do not show up as crisply as equivalent features on the surface of the Moon.

This image of the Earth was obtained by our old friend the Galileo space probe, looking back from a distance of about 1.3 million miles. South America is in the centre of the picture, with Antarctica clearly visible to the south, and weather fronts trail across the South Atlantic Ocean.

COSMIC IMPACT ON EARTH

Observations from space show that the surface of the Earth really is scarred with the traces of many impacts by objects from space, known collectively as meteorites. Both photographs and radar images from space highlight features that are not obvious from the ground, or even from aircraft. This particular impact crater (overleaf), in southwest Namibia, is shown in an image obtained from a space radar system carried on a flight of the space shuttle *Endeavour*, on 14 April 1994. The radar data have been converted into colours which highlight the structure of the crater, which is a relatively modest example of its kind, only 2.5 km wide and 130 metres deep (but the true bottom of the crater lies a further 100 metres below the surface of the sand that has partly filled it). It was formed by a meteorite that hit the Earth about 5 million years ago, just before our ancestors learned to walk upright. This crater is apparent at the surface of the Earth, but only the radar images reveal the detail of the structure and its full extent.

An impact like this in a populated region of the globe today would be a major disaster. The impact that wiped out the dinosaurs, 65 million years ago, produced a crater 180 km in diameter, which was buried by geological activity and has only recently been identified, in what is now the Yucatan Peninsula of Mexico. This is one of the biggest craters yet identified on the surface of the Earth (an impact that big occurs only every 100 million years or so), and the event that formed it was a terminal disaster as far as the dinosaurs and many other species were concerned.

But the demise of the dinosaurs opened the way for some creatures that survived the event to recover and thrive in a world free from dinosaurs. Among the most successful of these survivors were the mammals, our ancestors, to whom (with hindsight) that great meteorite impact can be seen as a lucky break. We owe our own origins directly to the blow from space that removed the dinosaurs from their dominant position on Earth, and opened up opportunities for other forms of life. But how those survivors from 65 million years ago survived and evolved to become us is another story.

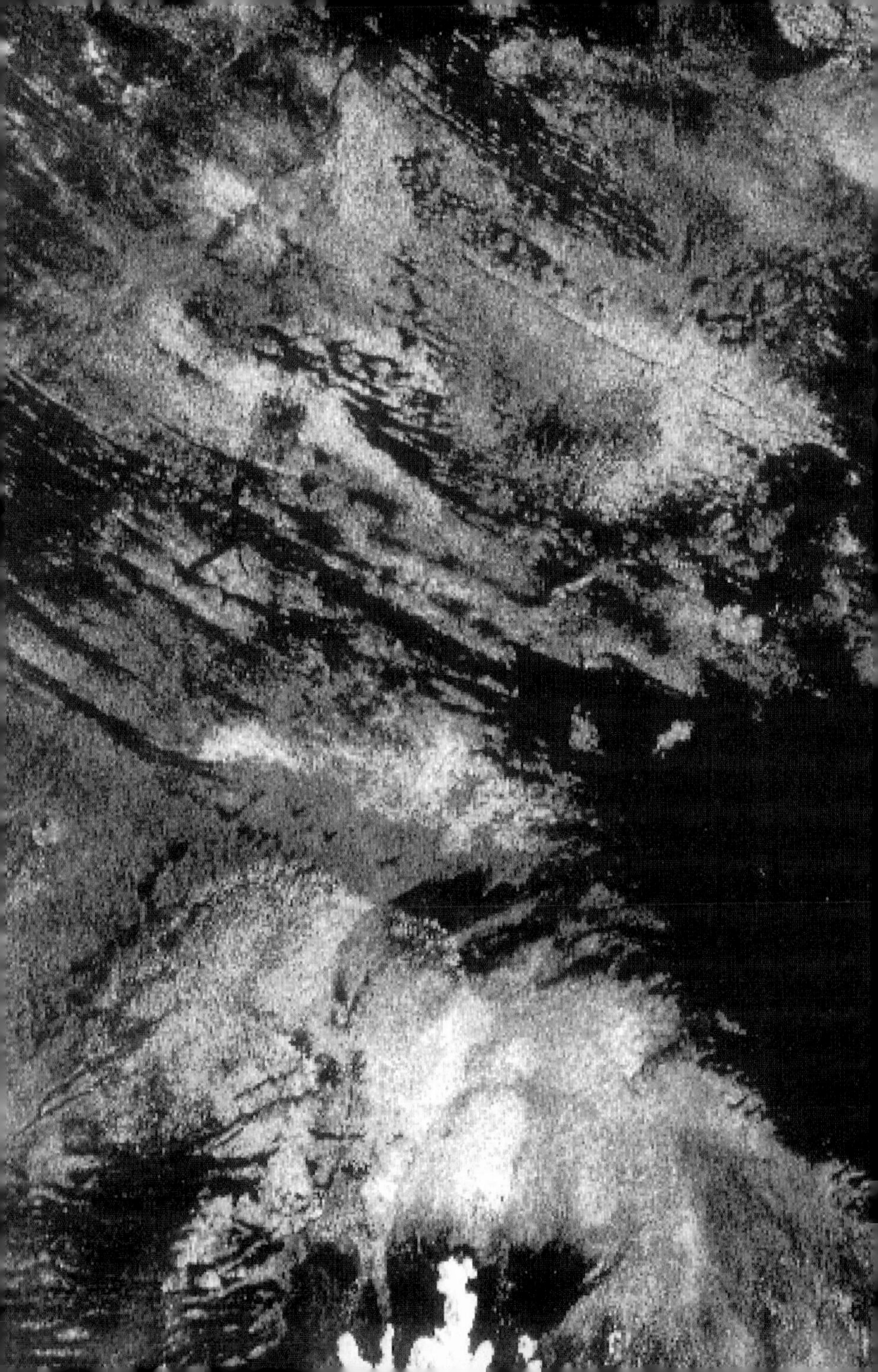

Part Two

Empire Of The Sun

Planets And Moons Of The Solar System

EMPIRE OF THE SUN
Planets And Moons Of The Solar System

In 1997, while the spaceprobe Galileo was sending back spectacular images from the planet Jupiter and its moons, a tiny robot explorer crawled around the surface of Mars, the Mars Global Surveyor spacecraft went into orbit around the planet, and, towards the end of the year, the Cassini probe blasted off for the ringed planet Saturn. This flurry of activity was part of the beginning of the second wave of the scientific exploration of the Solar System by unmanned craft, after a gap of nearly ten years since the probe Voyager 2 sent back images from Neptune, across 5 billion kilometres of space.

The first phase of this investigation of the Solar System had begun in 1959, when a probe launched by the Soviet Union flew past the Moon. In the same year the first photographs of the far side of the Moon, never seen from the surface of the Earth, were obtained. Over the next thirty years, culminating in the Voyager 2 flyby of Neptune in 1989, every planet in the Solar System (with the exception of Pluto, which is a peculiar object that should not really be classified as a planet at all) was visited by at least one probe. But though this transformed our scientific understanding of the nature of those planets and their moons – as well as providing spectacular images from the surfaces of these distant worlds – that whole era of planetary exploration should never be seen as anything more than a reconnaissance. To put it in perspective, after this first reconnaissance we had images of the other planets only slightly better than the views of the Moon that Galileo saw

Opposite: The farthest human beings have yet ventured into space is our nearest neighbour, the Moon. This shows an Apollo 17 astronaut driving the Lunar Rover in the Taurus-Littrow Valley.

when he first turned a telescope on its surface, early in the 17th century. The hiatus that followed was accidental, a result of a combination of factors. The changing political situation, with the break-up of the Soviet Union; economic factors; a shift of emphasis from 'pure' science to obtaining a better understanding of the planets in order to help solve problems, such as global warming, here on Earth; and, not least, the *Challenger* disaster, which delayed the departure of the Galileo probe for years, and led to a rethink of many aspects of the American space programme. But now that the second wave of exploration of the Solar System has begun, the data and images from the old probes are proving useful once again, providing a set of benchmarks against which the new observations can be compared. How would we know, for example, that some of the moons of Jupiter have changed since the 1980s, if the two Voyager probes had not been there in the 1980s? And, thanks to the dramatic improvements in computer power and image processing techniques in the past ten years (let alone since 1959), some of the old images have been processed in new ways, to produce both improved scientific data and even more spectacular visual delights.

Our aim in this section of the book is to focus unashamedly on the visual delights, offering you our selection of the best vistas of the Solar System that have yet been unveiled. We use some images from the first wave of planetary exploration (but usually dressed up in new, digitally enhanced finery), many from the new wave of planetary probes, and some from our old friend, the Hubble Space Telescope, which provides the best images we can get from Earth orbit of the other members of the Solar System. Of course, there

Opposite: From close orbit around the Earth, the thinness of the smear of atmosphere that supports life is clearly visible (see also Plate 56).

USA

will be more, and more spectacular, images to come, from the future probes that will explore Mars in more detail, from Cassini, and from missions that have yet even to reach the drawing board, let alone leave it. But that is no reason not to take stock now of the incredible variety of objects in our immediate cosmic neighbourhood. They really only have one thing in common: their membership of the Solar System. They are all gripped in the gravity of the Sun, which dominates its subjects more than any great emperor in history ever dominated his subjects. The empire of the Sun extends from the Sun itself out beyond even the orbit of Pluto, literally halfway to the nearest stars, where a cloud of frozen, icy bodies – the comets – is held in place by the Sun's gravity. We have images for you in this section of every kind of object known to exist in the Solar System, from the Sun itself to those comets, from planets to moons, and including the lumps of cosmic rubble known as asteroids.

But though our aim is primarily to entertain you with these breathtaking images, and to share with you our delight at the wonder they reveal, we shall not neglect the scientific side of the story entirely. When new discoveries are made in science, either by observation or as the result of new experiments, the observers or experimenters generally have mixed feelings about the way they want things to turn out. On the one hand, it would be nice if our cherished theories and ideas about the Universe were confirmed by the new observations and experiments. On the other hand, it would be exciting to discover something new and unexpected, which could form the basis of a better understanding of the Universe – or, at least, of one small corner of the Universe. The discoveries that have been made over recent decades about our Solar System – the Empire of the Sun – manage to please on both counts. The details have been astonishing and surprising. Nobody imagined for one moment that the moons of Jupiter, for

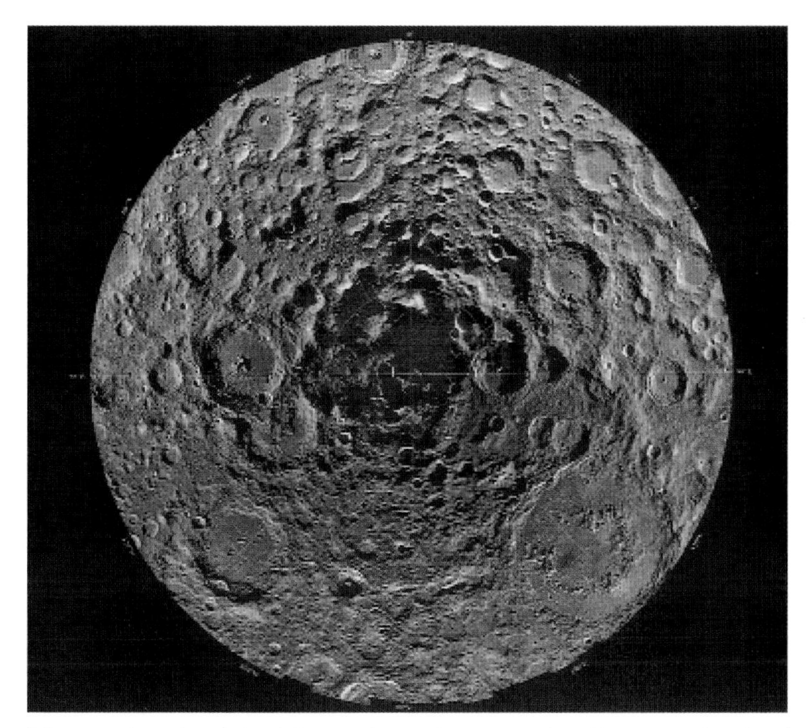

The south pole of the Moon, shown in a mosaic of images obtained by the Clementine spaceprobe.

example, would be so different from one another, or that some of them would be so geologically active. There are actually erupting volcanoes on Io, one of those moons, the first volcanoes to be seen erupting anywhere other than on Earth. Explaining the details of the new discoveries – exploring what amounts to the new Solar System – will keep astronomers busy for generations to come.

At the same time, though, the broad picture that has been revealed by the exploration of the Solar System so far confirms and strengthens our understanding of what the Solar System is, and how it came into being. We also touch on this in the context

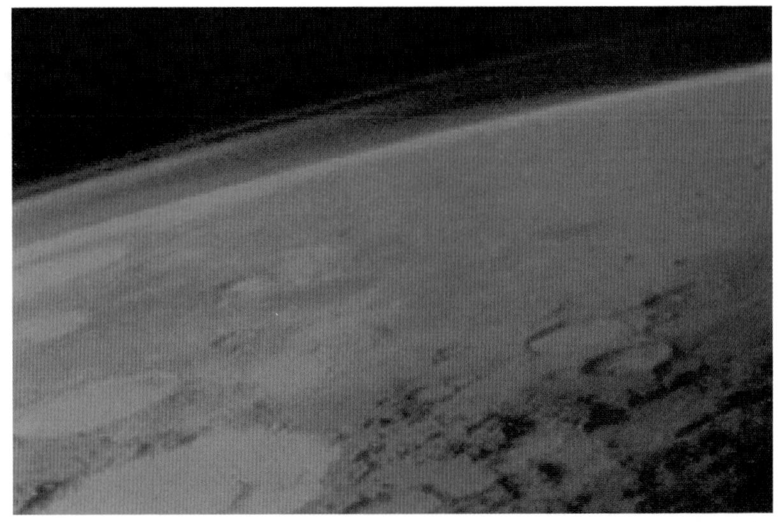

The striking difference between Mars and Earth is brought out by comparing this Viking Orbiter image with the blue Earth in Plate 56. A thin haze of carbon dioxide crystals can just be picked out in the atmosphere.

of the cosmological understanding of where the Universe itself, and the stars and galaxies within the Universe, came from. It is a stunning achievement of the human intellect to be able to say, with confidence, that the Universe had a definite beginning, and that this was between 13 and 15 billion years ago. But it is scarcely less stunning, by any everyday standards, to be able to say that the Solar System (including the Earth) had a definite beginning, and that it occurred about 4.5 billion years ago. So, to put the images you are about to see in context, we want to spell out in a little more detail this thorough modern understanding of how the Solar System formed, an account that has been amply confirmed by what the spaceprobes have found. Then we can give you at least a flavour of the mysteries remaining to be investigated when we deal with the individual planets and moons.

The Sun itself is a star – and a pretty ordinary star at that. It formed when a cloud of gas and dust in space collapsed, probably as a result of a large, nearby star exploding as a supernova. The collapsing cloud was almost certainly (judging from the clouds we see collapsing in this way in the Milky Way today) big enough to have formed dozens or hundreds of stars broadly similar to our Sun. These stars have gone their separate ways over the past few billion years and are now lost among the hundred billion stars of the Milky Way, the Galaxy in which we live. The cloud was chiefly composed of hydrogen and helium gas, left over from the Big Bang in which the Universe was born; but crucially, during the time since the Big Bang several previous generations of stars had run through their life cycles, and laced the interstellar medium with the debris ejected in their death-throes.

The nuclear reactions that keep stars shining during their lifetime work by fusing together nuclei of hydrogen to make more helium, and by successively sticking helium nuclei together, thereby building up elements such as carbon, nitrogen and oxygen. Other elements, such as uranium and lead, are manufactured in supernova explosions. Every element on Earth except the primordial hydrogen and helium has been manufactured inside stars and spread through space in this way; and the only reason that the Sun has a family of planets, including the Earth, made out of heavier elements is because it is a relative latecomer to the cosmic scene.

The Sun is a ball of hot gas (strictly speaking, a ball of plasma) which contains about 330,000 times as much mass as the Earth, in a sphere roughly 109 times as big in diameter as the Earth. It is made up of 71 per cent hydrogen by mass, and 26 per cent helium, with a smattering of heavier elements. The Sun makes up 99.86 per cent of the mass of the Solar System – everything else put together, all the planets, moons and cosmic rubble, makes up the remaining 0.14 per cent, and two-thirds of that is locked up in one planet, Jupiter.

With all this weight crushing inwards, the density at the heart of the Sun is twelve times that of solid lead (160 times the density of water), and the temperature is about 15 million degrees (on the absolute, or Kelvin scale, where the freezing point of water is 273 K; for all practical purposes, the temperature at the heart of the Sun can be thought of as 15 million degrees Celsius). Under these extreme conditions, even though the core of the Sun is so dense it behaves like a perfectly fluid gas. In the core, energy is released by nuclear fusion, as hydrogen nuclei are converted into helium nuclei. Along the way, each time a helium nucleus is made in this way a little mass is converted into energy, in line with Einstein's famous equation $E=mc^2$. Overall, to hold up the Sun against its own weight and keep it shining steadily, about 5 million tonnes of matter is converted into pure energy (ultimately, into sunlight) each second. Burning fuel at this prodigious rate, the Sun has lost about 4 per cent of its original stock from hydrogen over its 4.6 billion year lifetime to date. This energy emerges, in the form of light, from the visible surface of the Sun, which is at a temperature of about 6,000 K. But, as we shall see, the Sun itself extends beyond the visible surface, the form of tenuous streamers of gas reaching out into space, and even beyond the orbit of the Earth.

The planets can be divided neatly into two groups of four, each group made up of planets with similar properties to those of the other members of the group, and various kinds of cosmic rubble. A ninth object, Pluto, is usually called a planet for historical reasons. In fact, it is a rather large piece of cosmic rubble, more like a comet than anything else. We shall follow historical convention and dignify Pluto with the honorary title of 'planet', but we do not include it in our overall description of how the real planets formed. The two groups of planets whose origins need explaining are the four small, rocky objects (known as the terrestrial planets) which orbit close to the Sun, and the four large, gaseous planets (the gas giants) which orbit farther out.

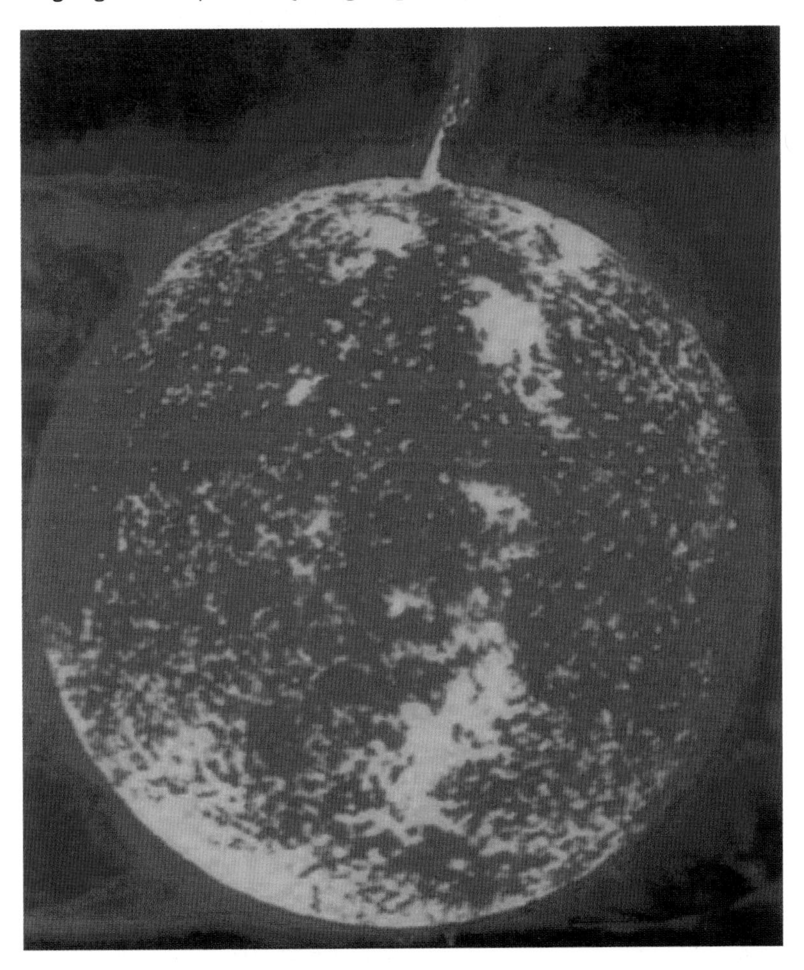

The Sun, ruler of the Solar System, shown here in an ultraviolet image obtained from Earth orbit during the Skylab missions.

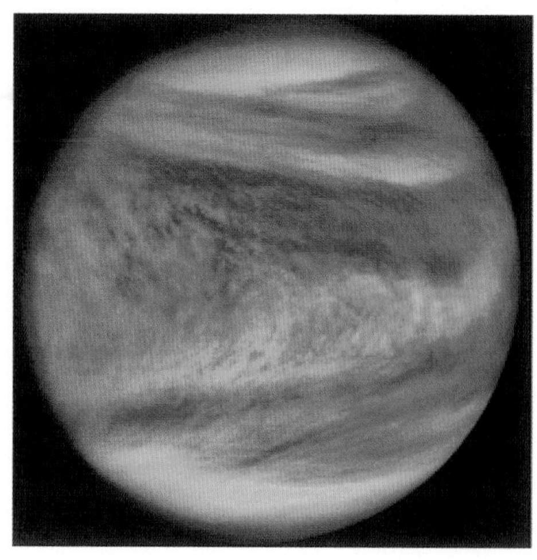

The sulphuric acid clouds of Venus, photographed by the Venus Orbiter probe in ultraviolet light.

Mercury is the closest planet to the Sun. It orbits the Sun once every 87.97 days, at an average distance of 0.39 AU. So when Mercury is exactly between us and the Sun, its distance from the Earth is only 0.61 AU; when it is on the opposite side of the Sun, it is 1.39 AU away (but can't be seen, of course, because the Sun is in the way). It has no atmosphere, a diameter of 4,880 km (intermediate in size between the Moon and Mars) and a mass one-twentieth that of the Earth.

Venus is the next planet out from the Sun, and comes nearer to the Earth than any other planet. It orbits the Sun once every 225 days at an average distance of 0.72 AU, so at its closest to us it approaches to 0.28 AU from Earth. It has a very dense

Opposite: The best views of Mars we can get from Earth orbit come from the Hubble Space Telescope. This image was obtained on 25 February 1995, when Mars was 103 million km from Earth.

atmosphere, chiefly carbon dioxide, a diameter of 12,104 km, and 82 per cent as much mass as the Earth.

The Earth itself is, as we all know, a rocky planet with a thin atmosphere and the only oceans of liquid water on any planet in the Solar System today. It is, by definition, at a distance of 1 AU from the Sun, and takes one year (365.26 days) to orbit the Sun once. It has a diameter of 12,756 km, and a mass of just under 6 thousand billion tonnes. The most distinctive astronomical feature of the Earth, though, is its relatively enormous Moon, which is the biggest in proportion to its parent planet of any moon in the Solar System (again, not counting Pluto as a planet). In many ways, the Earth-Moon system resembles a double planet, rather than a planet and its moon. Our Moon has a diameter of 3,476 km and a mass 1.2 per cent of the mass of the Earth. It was formed long ago, when the Solar System was young, when an object at least the size of Mars collided with the Earth. The collision generated so much heat that the entire surface crust of the Earth melted, and great globs of molten rock were flung into space, where they coalesced and formed the Moon. This model of the formation of the Moon explains why its composition is almost identical to the composition of the surface rocks of the Earth, and why it contains scarcely any water, which was all boiled away by the heat of the impact (the Earth's water is thought to have come from deep within the planet, released by volcanoes over geological time). The whole collision process can be modelled very accurately in a computer.

The last of the terrestrial planets is Mars. It orbits the Sun once every 686.98 days, at a distance varying between 1.38 and 1.67 AU. It has a very thin carbon dioxide atmosphere, a diameter of 6,795 km and a mass just over one-tenth the mass of the Earth (less than ten times the mass of the Moon).

Beyond the orbit of Mars there is a region, from about 1.7 to 4 AU from the Sun, in which many pieces of cosmic rubble orbit the Sun in a ring, rather like the rings of Saturn but on a much larger scale. The orbital periods of these objects, the asteroids, are between 3 and 6 years. It is estimated that there are more than a million of them which are each at least a kilometre across in this ring of cosmic debris, plus many more smaller objects. Asteroids whose orbits are accurately known are given numbers, and many also have names. The largest of the asteroids, or minor planets as they are sometimes called, is Ceres, with a diameter of 933 km;

The Mars Global Surveyor spaceprobe sent back this detailed image of part of the surface of Mars soon after it went into orbit around the red planet in September 1997. It shows part of a feature called Nirgal Vallis. Because of problems adjusting the orbit of the spacecraft, it did not begin its full mapping mission until March 1999 when it sent back images showing features ten times smaller than the smallest shown here.

but only 10 minor planets (including Ceres) are bigger than 250 km across. The asteroids are the remains of failed planets that were prevented from coalescing and forming planets when the Solar System was young, but were smashed into one another by the gravitational pull of Jupiter, disturbing their orbits. But most of the original mass in the asteroid belt has been lost, as objects have been ejected by Jupiter's gravity, perturbing them into orbits that sent them crashing into the other planets (including the collision that formed the Moon), or out of the Solar System altogether. Today, the total mass of all the asteroids in the belt put together is only about 15 per cent of the mass of the Moon.

Jupiter itself, the first and grandest of the gas giants, lies beyond the asteroid belt at a distance of 5.2 AU from the Sun. It orbits the Sun once every 11.86 years. It has a diameter 11 times that of the Earth, and a mass 0.1 per cent that of the Sun, more than twice as much mass as all the other planets, moons and bit of rubble in the Solar System put together. Jupiter has its own mini-empire, a family of at least 16 moons (there may well be further small ones awaiting discovery) and a faint ring system. Unlike the terrestrial planets (but like the other gas giants), Jupiter is mainly composed of hydrogen and helium gas. It is more like a failed star than a planet in the terrestrial sense.

Saturn orbits the Sun at a distance varying between 9 and 10 AU, taking 29.46 years to complete each orbit. It has a diameter at the equator 9.4 times the diameter of the Earth, and a mass 95 times the mass of the Earth. Like Jupiter, it is accompanied by a family of moons; it also has a spectacular ring system, one of the visual highlights of any tour of the Solar System.

Uranus, the seventh planet out from the Sun, orbits at a distance varying between 18.3 and 20.1 AU, taking 84 years to complete each orbit. It has a diameter just over four times that of the Earth (modest for a gas giant) and a mass 14.5 times that of the Earth.

Neptune, the farthest real planet from the Sun, orbits once every 164.79 years, at a distance of 30.06 AU. Since it was only discovered in 1846, this means that astronomers have not yet had the opportunity to watch one complete orbit of Neptune around the Sun; no doubt they will find a suitable way to mark the occasion, in 2011, when the first observed orbit is completed. Neptune has a diameter 3.8 times the diameter of the Earth, and a mass of 17.2 times that of the Earth, so it is very similar to Uranus. Both Uranus and Neptune have large families of moons.

Pluto is a planetary wanderer, discovered in 1930, with a highly elliptical orbit which varies between about 30 AU (taking it closer

Jupiter, viewed by the spaceprobe Voyager 1 as it approached the giant planet early in 1979. The moon Io can be seen in front of the face of Jupiter, just below centre right of the picture.

to the Sun than Neptune) and 50 AU. At its farthest, light from the Sun takes seven hours to reach Pluto. It has a mass only 0.3 per cent that of the Earth (about twice that of our Moon), and a moon, Charon, which is more than half as big as Pluto and orbits at a distance of only 19,400 km (our Moon orbits the Earth at a distance of 384,400 km). Pluto and Charon are both probably icy chunks of debris typical of a swarm of pieces of cosmic icebergs that litter the region of space beyond the orbit of Neptune. This ring of iceberg-like supercomets is called the Kuiper Belt.

Far beyond the Kuiper Belt lies the Oort Cloud, a spherical shell of cometary icebergs surrounding the Solar System, between about 50,000 and 100,000 AU from the Sun, so distant that light takes one and a half years to get from the Sun to the Oort Cloud. But even this far out into space, in the far reaches of the Empire of the Sun, the comets are still held in orbit around the Sun by gravity. The cloud may contain as many as 100 billion comets, each one an icy lump travelling in a long, slow orbit around the Sun. From time to time, something (perhaps the nearby passage of another star) will shake some of these comets loose, and send them falling in towards the Sun on orbits that will take millions of years to bring them in to our part of the Solar System.

There, the heat from the Sun boils away gas from the comet, often producing a spectacular tail of tenuous material that shines in reflected sunlight as the comet swings around the Sun and heads back into the depths of space. Sometimes, comets are trapped by the gravity of Jupiter and diverted, like the famous Halley's Comet, into orbits that bring them swinging through the inner Solar System every few decades. In 1997, the spectacular visit of Comet Hale-Bopp to the inner Solar System reminded us all of the beauty of these objects; together with the impact of Shoemaker-Levy 9 with Jupiter in 1994, Hale-Bopp also reminded us that

Saturn, viewed by the Hubble Space Telescope in September 1990. Although this was before the flaw in the optics of the HST was corrected, this highly detailed image was produced by combining three separate images of Saturn from the Wide Field and Planetary Camera and using computer enhancement to bring out the detail.

occasionally during the long history of the Earth our planet has been struck by one of these visitors from space, wreaking terrible devastation. The death of the dinosaurs, 65 million years ago, is thought to have been caused by such an event.

But how did the plants and comets (and the rest of the cosmic rubble) get there in the first place? The explanation takes us back to the birth of the Solar System, as just one localised collapsing region of a larger cloud of collapsing gas and dust, squeezed into collapse by the blast wave from a nearby supernova, 4.6 billion years ago.

As far as the existence of the planets is concerned, the key feature of the Solar System is the way material is organised in a thin disk, with essentially all of the material in the disk moving the same way around the Sun. When the cloud that collapsed to form the Solar System started to collapse, it must have been rotating, if only a little – it would be an extraordinarily unlikely cloud that just hung in space without rotating at all.

As that cloud collapsed, the rotation would have got faster and faster, just as spinning ice-skaters spin faster if they pull their arms inwards. The relationship between how fast an object is spinning, how big it is and how massive it is, is measured in terms of a property called angular momentum, and angular momentum alone would have been able to stop the spinning cloud contracting, holding it up against gravity, so the Sun would never have formed – unless some of the angular momentum could be got rid of.

Obviously, the 'protosun' did get rid of enough angular momentum, or we would not be here pondering these puzzles today. This happened partly because the protosun ejected material into space, carrying angular momentum away with it, and partly because some of the material in the cloud settled into a disk around the young star. Angular momentum depends on how far the mass concerned is from the centre of rotation, as well as the amount of mass and how fast it is moving. So Jupiter, even though it is much less massive than the Sun, carries a great deal of angular momentum because it is not only big (for a planet) but far from the centre of the Sun. And the other objects in the Solar System also help to restore angular momentum that would otherwise have prevented the Sun from forming at all.

In the disk of the Solar System, all the planets (including Jupiter) orbit the Sun in the same direction. Most of the planets have moons, and with very few exceptions the moons orbit the planets in the same direction that the planets orbit the Sun (the exceptions are thought not to be original moons, formed *in situ* when the Solar System was born, but lumps of rubble captured by

Cosmic rubble. Three asteroids, photographed separately by the Galileo spaceprobe, put together as a montage by NASA.

their parent planets at a later date; one might call them foster moons). Even the rotation of the planets is turning them on their axes in the same direction (with the exception of Uranus and Venus, which may have had their spin changed by impacts with large pieces of cosmic rubble). And the Sun itself, turning on its axis once every 25.3 days, rotates in the same direction again. All this is powerful evidence that the planets and (most of) the moons did form at the same time as the Sun, out of a thin disk of material thrown out from the collapsing protosun. The material in the disk condensed to form planets, and for the larger planets the whole process repeated in miniature, with families of moons growing up around those planets in the same way that a family of planets grew up around the Sun.

The easiest thing to explain is why there are two kinds of planet in the Solar System – small, rocky planets near the Sun, and large, gaseous planets farther out. It was all thanks to the heat of the young Sun, which blew the more volatile material away from the inner regions of the Solar System, leaving it to condense out farther from the Sun, where the temperature was lower.

Planet-building must have begun in the original gas cloud before material had even started to form a disk around the protosun. Tiny grains of dust in the cloud would have collided with one another and stuck together to make fluffy supergrains, each a few millimetres across. Because these grains were constantly being bombarded by molecules of gas in the increasingly dense collapsing cloud, they would have been very susceptible to the processes which transfer angular momentum, and would have settled quickly into the disk (literally being pushed into place), giving them ample opportunity for further interactions with one another.

At first, the stickiness of these supergrains was what mattered – they would collide gently together, because they were moving in the same direction around the Sun in the disk, so they would not be disrupted in the collisions and would join together. By the time these primordial pebbles had grown to about the size of asteroids, perhaps 1km or so across, their own gravity would have become important, tugging groups of asteroids together in swarms, encouraging collisions and interactions which made bigger lumps. But head-on collisions, which would have disrupted the lumps, were rare, because everything was moving in the same direction. The bigger lumps, with the strongest gravitational influence, then swallowed up the rest of the rubble in their immediate orbital vicinity, sweeping a clean path around the Sun. Those larger lumps became the planets – and the evidence of this final 'sweeping up' process is visible on the battered faces of planets and moons.

Never seen from the Earth, the far side of the Moon was imaged by the Galileo spaceprobe as it set off on its voyage to Jupiter. The colouring in this image indicates the different kinds of surface material present on the Moon (see also Plate 64).

As the objects that were to become the planets grew in this way, the young Sun was glowing at the heart of the cloud of gas and dust in which they were forming. Close to the Sun, the heat was enough to drive out any material that was easily volatilised, so that growing clumps of matter were dominated by substances that are not easily volatilised, such as iron and silica. Farther out from the Sun, though, the original grains from the interstellar cloud that collapsed to form the Solar System would retain a coating of icy material, including water-ice, frozen methane and frozen ammonia. And as large lumps of material started to accumulate far out from the Sun, their gravitational pull was sufficient to trap some of the hydrogen and helium being blown out from the heart of the original gas cloud by the activity of the young star at its centre.

Beyond the orbit of Jupiter, there must have been a huge amount of this frozen stuff, forming very many ice-balls. Some of these icebergs accumulated to form what became the inner cores of the other giant planets; but the gravitational influence of Jupiter itself soon dominated what went on in this region of the disk. Some of the Ice-balls were diverted into orbits taking them close by the Sun, where they evaporated entirely after a few orbits. Others smashed into the inner planets (there is a school of thought which says that this is where most of the Earth's water came from, with only a 'topping up' from volcanic eruptions). But many were deflected outwards, in a kind of gravitational slingshot effect, where they formed the Kuiper Belt and the Oort Cloud.

A recent calculation, based on computer simulations of this process, suggests that there were initially about 120 Earth masses of icy material in the region beyond Jupiter and within the present-day orbit of Neptune. Of this, 85 Earth masses went to

Opposite: Comet Hale-Bopp, photographed here from the surface of the Earth using an ordinary 35 mm SLR camera, passed through the inner Solar System in 1997. The spectacle provided by the comet's two tails, clearly visible here, was the result of heat from the Sun boiling material away from the dirty ice-ball that formed the nucleus of the comet (see Plate 72).

make the cores of Saturn, Uranus and Neptune, with gas accreting onto those cores by gravity. So 35 Earth masses of primordial material were left over in the form of cometary icebergs. Half were perturbed into orbits taking them close by the Sun, and 16 Earth masses of cometary material went the other way, being ejected from the Solar System entirely to roam interstellar space. Just 1.5 Earth masses of material were left to form the Oort Cloud. The Solar System was complete, and the boundary of the Empire of the Sun had been defined.

And all of this was a natural consequence of the collapse of a cloud of gas in space, laced with a smattering of dust in the form of interstellar grains – dust that had itself been formed out of elements forged in the nuclear furnaces of previous generations of stars. There is no reason to doubt that every time a star forms in this way it will be accompanied by a retinue of planets not unlike the Solar System. Very many stars, as it happens, do not form in isolation in quite this way: they form multiple systems, with two or three (or more) stars in orbit around one another. But whenever a star does form in isolation – and that means many millions of stars in the disk of the Milky Way alone, even allowing for them being a small minority of the stellar population – planets like those in our Solar System must form as well. In all probability, this means that life – even intelligent life – may be quite common, and that at this very moment there are other civilisations exploring other planetary worlds, and marvelling over the images being sent back to their home planet. The Empire of the Sun is special to us, but it is surely not unique. As we sit back and enjoy a guided tour of the best views in the Solar System, it is worth keeping in mind the possibility that one day this may all seem as parochial as a medieval European map of 'the world', bounded by the Mediterranean Sea and the Atlantic Ocean, with more distant regions simply marked 'Here be Dragons'.

Empire Of The Sun

Planets And Moons Of The Solar System

The Pictures

SUNRISE FROM APOLLO 12

For many people, the first time they began to have any true feeling for the fragility of our home in space came at the end of the 1960s, when the Apollo missions brought back the first images of the Earth as a planet. Our tour of the Solar System begins with the sun, which sits at the centre of its planetary empire; but it also begins with the Earth, the oasis in space on which we live. This simple but striking image was obtained by the astronauts of Apollo 12 on their journey home from the Moon in November 1969. It shows the Sun just emerging from an eclipse, when the Earth passed directly between the returning spacecraft and the Sun. The thinness of the atmosphere – the life zone of our planet – is dramatically highlighted by this view, and rainbow-like stripes of colour can be seen at either end of the arc of atmosphere illuminated by the rising Sun.

A SOLAR FLARE, SEEN FROM SKYLAB

On 19 December 1973, during the third and last manned Skylab mission, the astronauts in orbit around the Earth witnessed one of the most spectacular solar flares ever recorded. The arc of ionised gas (plasma) sent climbing into space by this event spanned more than 588,000 km, about one and a half times the distance from the Earth to the Moon. This photograph was taken in light at the extreme ultraviolet part of the spectrum, at wavelengths too short to be visible to human eyes, produced by energetic helium atoms. Active regions on the surface of the Sun show up as bright patches at these wavelengths.

This kind of activity comes and goes with a rhythm roughly 11 years long, known as the solar cycle. The Sun was building towards a peak of activity at the end of the 1990s.

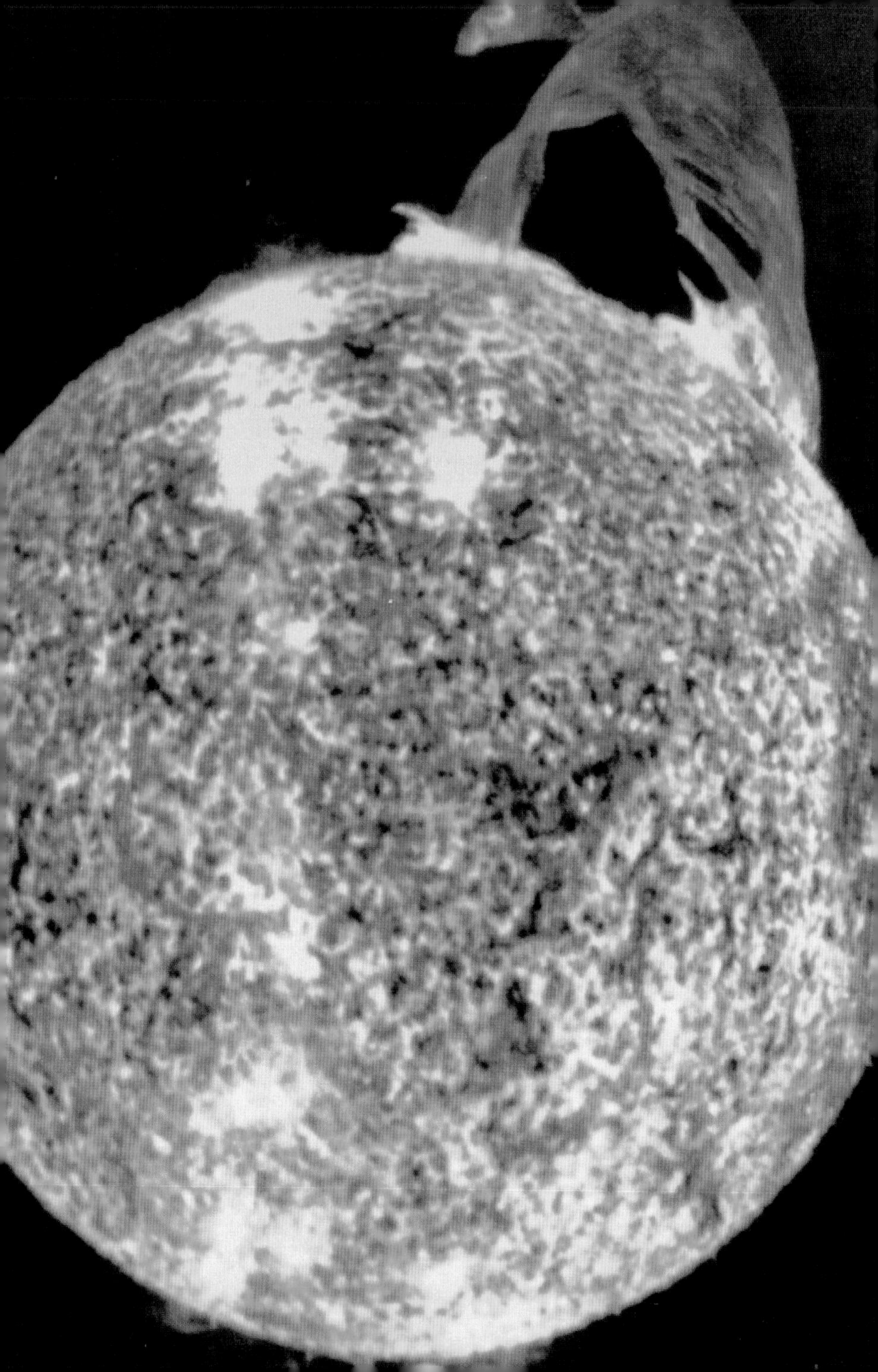

THE OUTER REGIONS OF THE SUN

Because the surface of the Sun is so bright, neither the human eye nor cameras can detect the relatively faint atmosphere of the Sun, except during an eclipse, when the Moon conveniently blocks out the light from the Sun itself. Borrowing a trick from nature, astronomers make artificial eclipses by placing a disk of material, just big enough to obscure the main image of the Sun, in front of their detectors. In this composite image obtained by detectors on board the unmanned SOHO spacecraft, one detector has looked directly at the Sun, while a separate detector has simultaneously observed the outer atmosphere by using the artificial eclipse technique. The two images have then been put together to give a picture of how hot material streams away from the surface of the Sun and out into space in all directions.

The surface of the Sun itself and its lower atmosphere (inside the dark circle) are seen here in the ultraviolet light emitted by highly ionised (electrically charged) iron atoms, at a temperature of 2 million degrees Celsius; the outer atmosphere is seen by the light of ionised oxygen atoms, at a temperature of 200 million degrees Celsius, escaping into space. The composite image clearly shows that the hottest and most active (brightest) regions in the escaping gas are directly above the active (bright) regions on the solar surface.

SOLAR BLUES

Everyone has heard of a 'blue Moon' – but a blue Sun? This image is, strictly speaking, a 'false colour' view since no human eyes could ever see the light that was used to obtain it, in the extreme ultraviolet region of the spectrum, bluer than the bluest visible light. It was taken by an instrument on board the SOHO probe, as part of a sequence that shows the dynamic activity of the ever-changing surface of the Sun (even when the Sun is at a relatively low level of activity overall) as a movie recorded in real time. The activity that is imaged in this way is seen in the thin atmosphere of the Sun, the region known as the corona which lies just inside the dark circle in Plate 45, where the temperature reaches more than a million degrees Celsius and produces intense ultraviolet radiation from atoms of iron which have been stripped of many of their electrons.

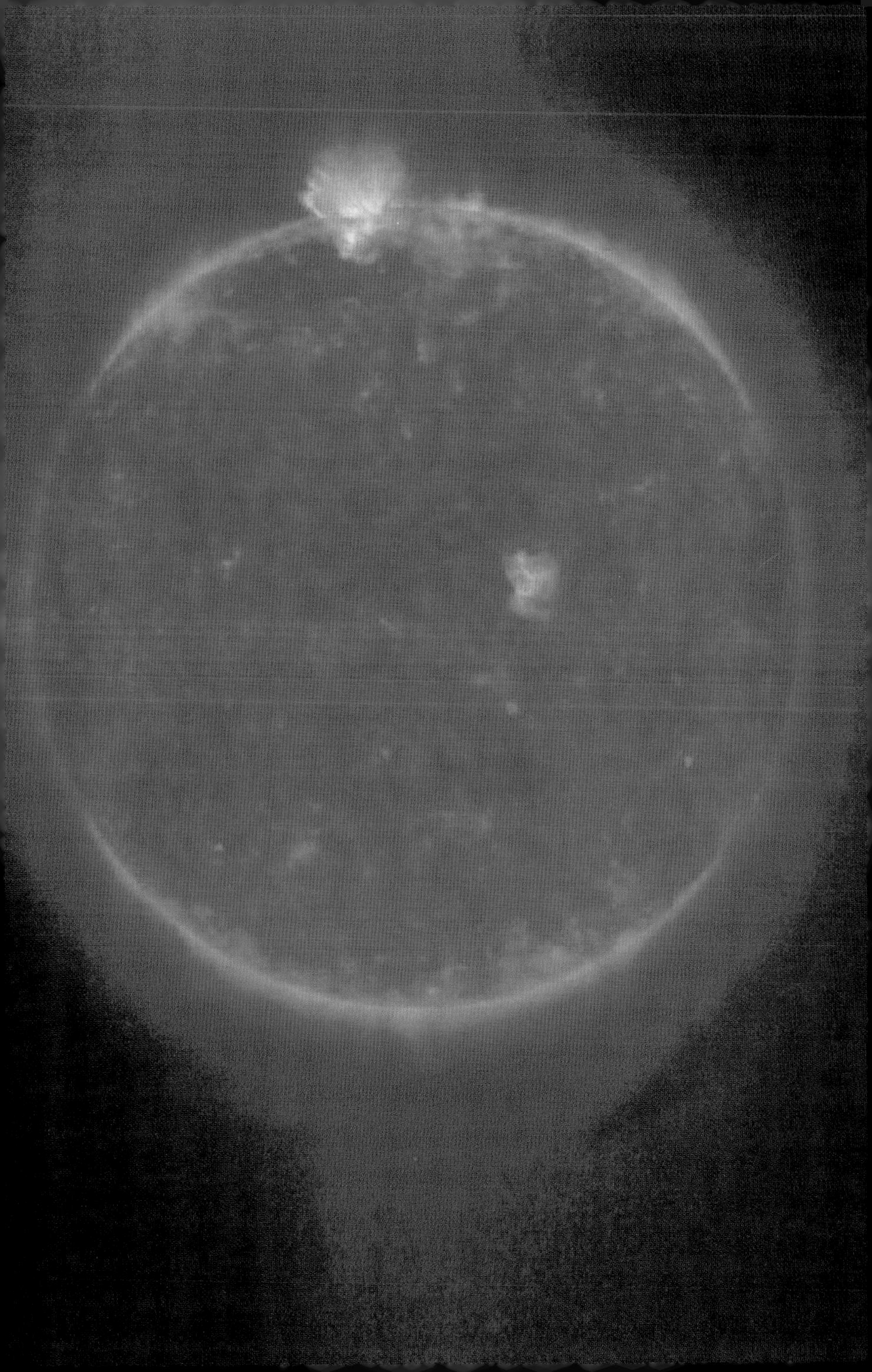

MERCURY

Mercury is the closest planet to the Sun. This makes it very difficult to study using telescopes on Earth, because when the planet is on the same side of the Sun as us we can only see its night side, while when it is on the other side of the Sun it is hidden in the glare of the Sun itself. The first time astronomers had any idea what the surface of Mercury was like was when the spaceprobe Mariner 10 made the first of three flybys past the planet in 1974. The face of Mercury turned out to bear a striking resemblance to the surface of our Moon, with many craters bearing witness to the battering it had received when the Solar System was young. This was one of the key pieces of evidence which helped to establish the modern understanding of the formation of the planets, outlined previously.

This mosaic of Mariner 10 images gives a good impression of the overall appearance of Mercury, even though you can see the joins where individual photographs have been put together. Colour has been added to highlight the surface features.

MERCURY IN CLOSE-UP

Although Mariner 10 was one of the first wave of spaceprobes to open up our understanding of the Solar System, no subsequent probe has since visited Mercury (the Mercury Messenger probe launched from Cape Canaveral in August 2004 and is due to reach its destination in 2011). So the best images we have of the surface of the innermost planet are all three decades old and, as this close-up shows, lack the crisp detail of some of the other images in this book. Nevertheless, close-ups sent back by Mariner 10, like this one, are invaluable because they show no sign of volcanoes or other geological activity. It is quite clear that Mercury is a dead planet, and that the craters on its surface were made by impacts long ago, not by volcanoes. Very little has happened on the surface of Mercury for more than 3 billion years.

The colour that has been added to this image may give a more accurate idea of how the planet would look to the human eye.

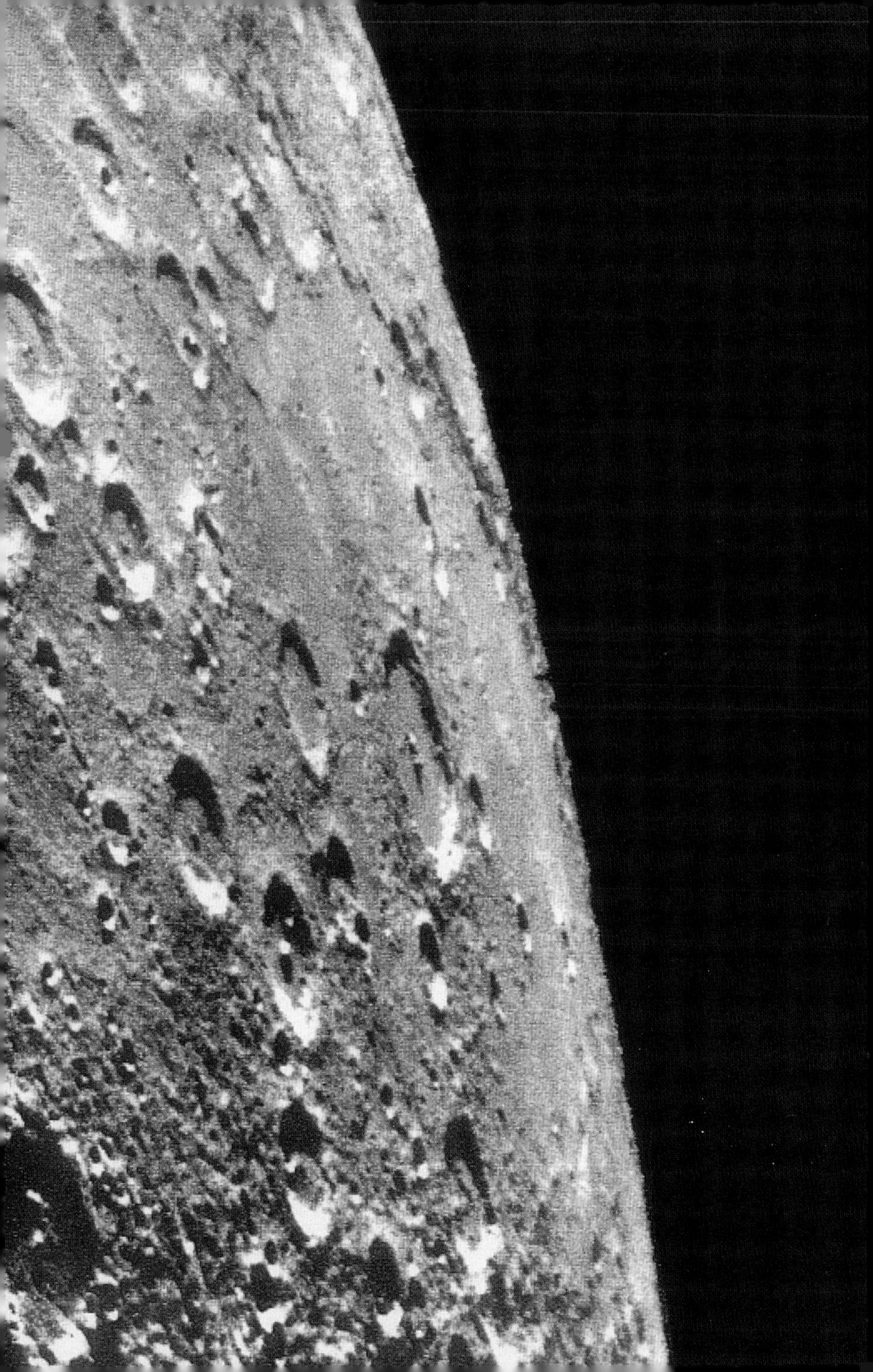

THE CLOUDS OF VENUS

If Mercury is difficult to observe, Venus is an Earth-based astronomer's nightmare. As well as lying between us and the Sun, which raises the same observational problem as posed by Mercury, unlike Mercury Venus is covered by a thick atmosphere and swathed in clouds. So even a passing spaceprobe cannot obtain a direct image of the surface. This picture, taken by the probe Galileo from a distance of 2.7 million km in February 1990, highlights the problem. All we can see are the sulphuric acid clouds, streaked by their rapid westward movement at speeds of up to 100 metres per second.

Had any human astronauts been on board Galileo, they would not have seen even this much detail. To human eyes, the clouds of Venus are a featureless white smear. The structure in the photograph has been revealed by taking it through a violet filter, and then colouring the resulting image blue to enhance the contrast.

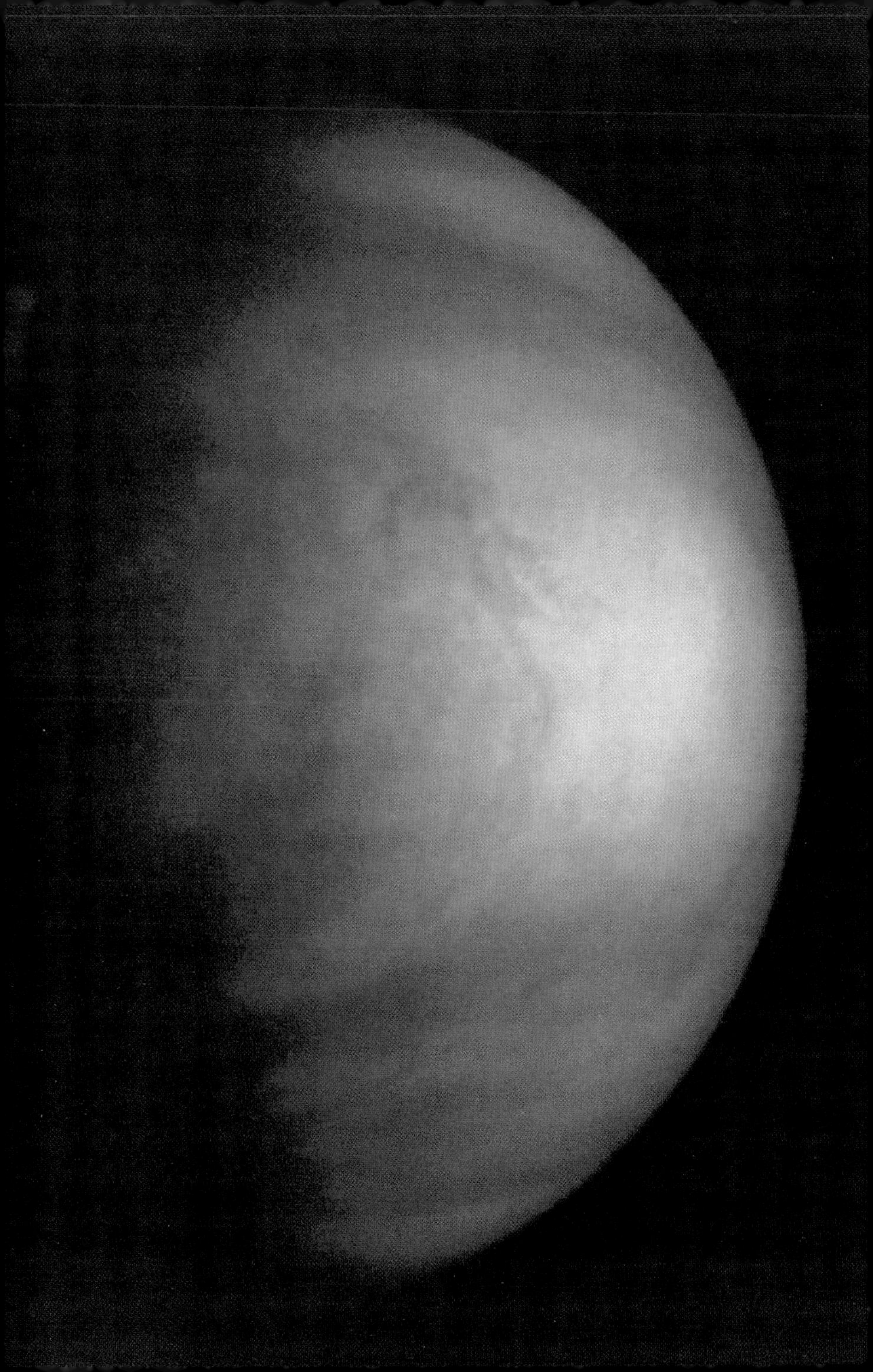

THE SURFACE OF VENUS

The only pictures we have from the surface of Venus were obtained by the Soviet Venera probes in 1982. Venera 13, which reached the surface on 1 March 1982, sent back fourteen pictures, including this one, during the 2 hours and 7 minutes that it survived before being simultaneously cooked, crushed and corroded by the heat, pressure and acid rain. This colour image was obtained by combining information from three images taken through dark blue, green and red filters; it is a panoramic view, covering 170 degrees, with part of the spacecraft visible at the bottom of the photograph. Part of the horizon has been cut off by the angle at which the camera scanned. The object on the ground in the foreground is a lens cover from one of the cameras.

Although the picture clearly shows both rocks and soil on the surface of Venus, it is difficult to judge what the true colour of this material is, because the atmosphere of Venus filters out blue light. But the images from Venera 13 (and its companion probe Venera 14) provide the best guide we have to what the colour of the surface of Venus would be if the obscuring atmosphere and clouds were stripped away.

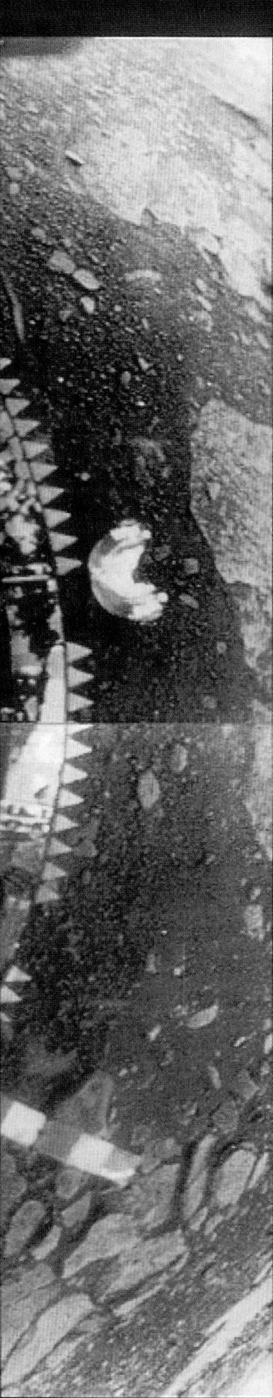

PROBING VENUS'S SURFACE

Although visible light cannot penetrate the clouds of Venus, radar can. Astronomers first bounced radar signals from Earth off Venus in the 1960s, and began to get information about its surface topography that way. In the 1970s, the NASA probe Pioneer Venus and two Soviet probes, Venera 15 and Venera 16, went into orbit around Venus, and used radar to probe its surface in more detail. But the veils of Venus were finally ripped away by the Magellan probe, which went into orbit around Venus in 1990, and used radar to map almost the entire surface in such detail that it revealed features only 100 metres across. By combining these topographic maps with colour information about the surface rocks from the Venera 13 and 14 missions, astronomers have been able to produce computer-generated virtual reality images of how the surface of Venus would look if it were not obscured by cloud; some of these stunning images are shown on the next few pages.

The most striking overall feature of the surface of Venus is that, unlike Mercury, it is clearly an active planet where geological processes continue to the present day. This particular image shows pancake volcanoes, produced by lava oozing out from molten layers below the surface of the planet and spreading across the surface. The domes are about 25 km across and 750m high, and are shown as if they were being viewed from an altitude of 2.4 km. The vertical scale has been exaggerated in this image to bring out the detail of these structures.

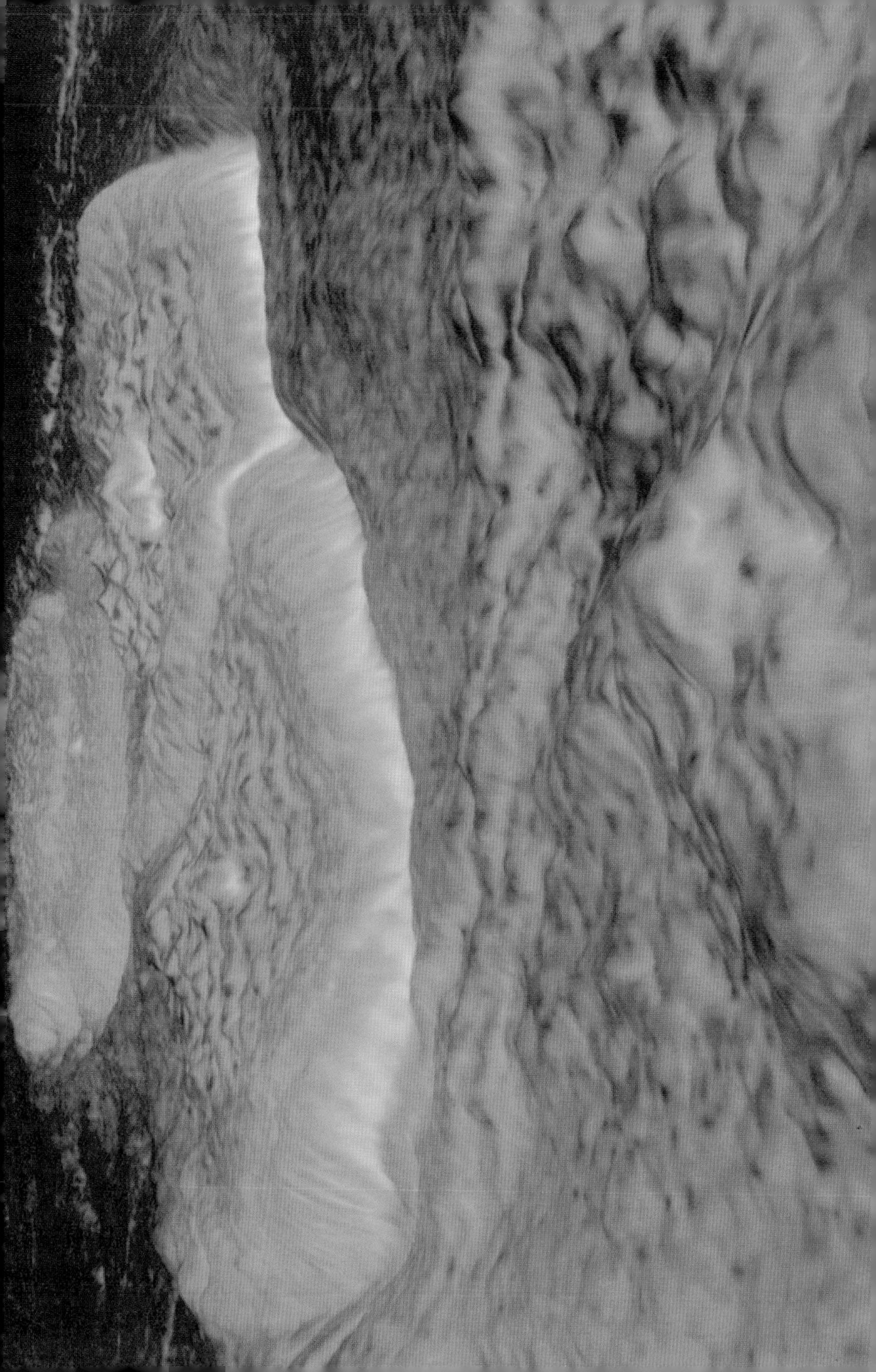

A VENUSIAN VOLCANO

This is an example of the detail that is present in the Magellan radar data. The image, which covers an area of about 250,000 km^2, is centred on an unnamed volcano that is about 2 km high. The colours have been chosen to indicate the temperature of the rocks around the volcano, red corresponding to high temperatures and blue to (relatively) low temperatures.

This kind of volcano is common on Venus, and bears a clear family resemblance to the shield volcanoes of the Earth – classic cone-shaped structures like the volcanoes of Hawaii.

COUNTING CRATERS

As well as its geological activity, the surface of Venus is also scarred by many large impact craters. The view overleaf is of a group dubbed the 'crater farm', and is made up of Saskia (37.3 km across, in the foreground), Danilove (47.6 km across, to the left) and Aglaonice (62.6 km across, to the right). Once again, the topographic detail comes from Magellan, and the colouring is based on data from Veneras 13 and 14.

Images like this help to confirm that the inner planets of the Solar System have been battered by cosmic impacts. But a comparison of the number of craters visible on the face of Venus and the number visible on the surfaces of other planets shows that something spectacular happened to Venus about 600 million years ago. There are far fewer craters on Venus than there would be if, like Mercury and the Moon, it had retained its original scarred surface layer. From the counts of craters, astronomers infer that the surface of Venus was wiped clean in some geological upheaval that completely resurfaced the planet with fresh lavas about 600 million years ago, and that this may have been only the most recent of several such events in the planet's 4-billion-year history.

This focuses alarmingly on the continuing impact threat in the inner Solar System today. It implies that all of the cratering seen on the face of Venus now, including the 'farm' opposite, has happened in the relatively recent geological past, and that objects big enough to cause craters as large as these still roam the inner Solar System. The Earth, as well as Venus, is at risk from such objects, and has also been subjected to a similar bombardment from space over the same sort of timescale – as the dinosaurs discovered to their cost.

Tantalisingly, the resurfacing of Venus occurred at about the time of the first great diversification of life in the oceans of Earth, after billions of years of stagnation. Nobody knows if this is anything more than a coincidence.

VENUS IN PERSPECTIVE

Like Plate 52, this perspective view of a region of Venus known as Sedna Planitia has been colour-coded to indicate the temperature of different regions of the surface. The low-lying regions of Venus are marked by several features like this, in which depressions surrounded by fracture patterns (known as coronae) form lines along the planet's tectonic belts (not unlike the volcanic 'ring of fire' that bounds the Pacific Ocean on Earth). It is thought that the coronae are caused by 'hot spots' beneath the surface of Venus, which first push magma up and lift the surface, then cool and contract so that the surface slumps into a depression and the surrounding rocks crack in this distinctive way. Sometimes the lava escapes onto the surface; it can be seen in this image as bright flows of material in the image.

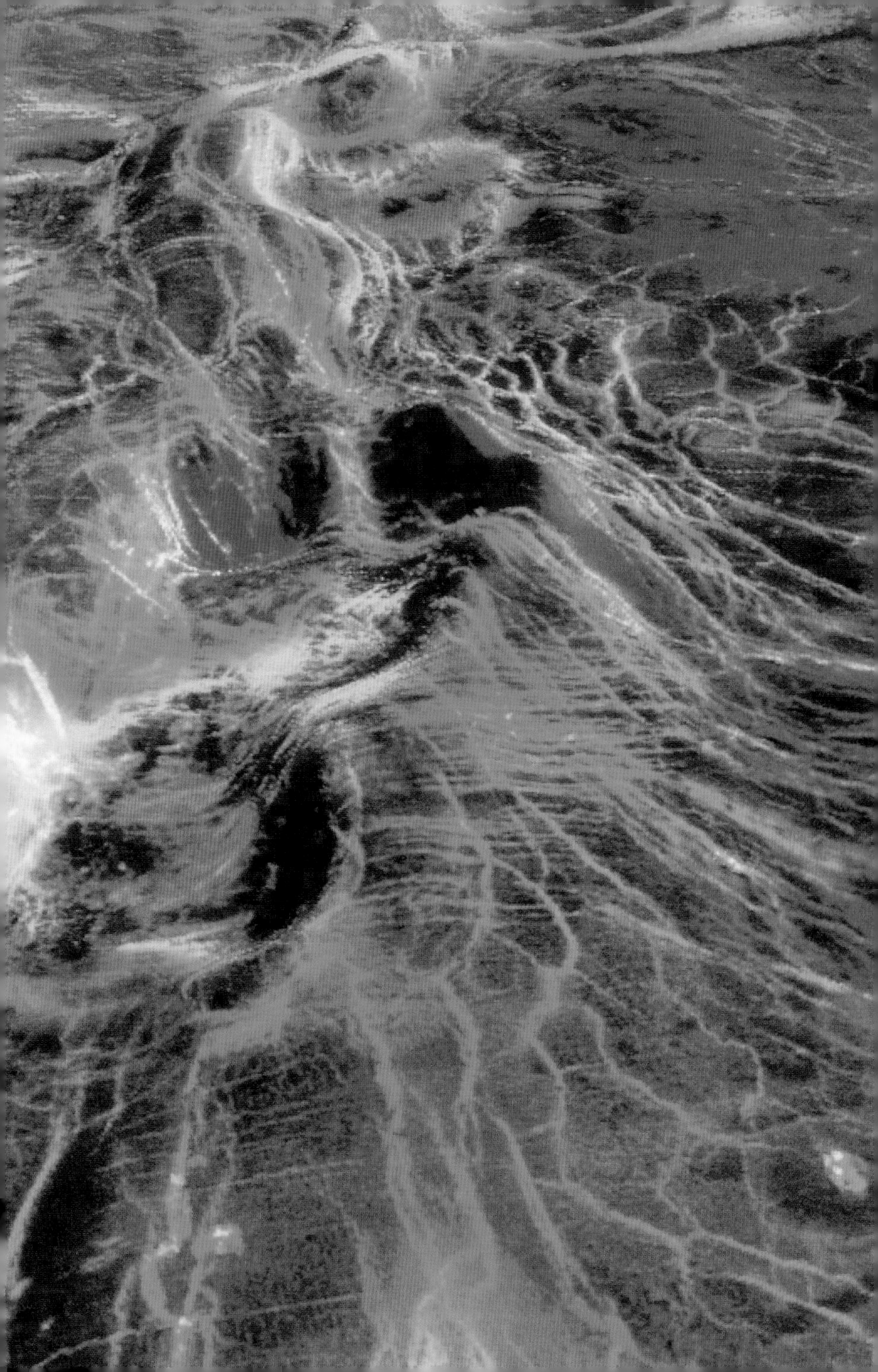

VENUS UNVEILED

Many years of work went into producing this image of one hemisphere of Venus as it would appear if the planet had no atmosphere. Most of the data used to make it comes from Magellan, which sent back data from Venus from 1990 to 1994; but gaps have been filled in with radar imagery and altitude information from Pioneer Venus, from Veneras 15 and 16, and even from ground-based radar studies made using the Arecibo radio telescope in Puerto Rico. Imagery from Magellan itself covered more than 98 per cent of Venus at a resolution of about 100 m; the smallest features visible in this mosaic are about 3 km across. The colours in this image are not intended to represent the true colour of the surface of Venus, but are coded to indicate the varying elevation of the surface (rather like a colour contour map) and to emphasise contrast.

OASIS EARTH

The image of the fragile Earth floating in space like a beautiful blue marble, with a scarcely discernible skin of atmosphere maintaining the life zone around our planet, has become a cliché of the space age. Cliché or not, the image is more than 30 years old, dating from the Apollo missions of the late 1960s; and it does convey a genuine sense of our place in the Universe, putting human civilisation with its hopes, fears and conflicts in a cosmic perspective. This particular photograph of the nearly full Earth was taken by the astronauts of Apollo 15, and shows South America just left of centre, Central America, Mexico and Florida can be seen at the upper left, while Spain and northwest Africa are visible at the upper right. The image was taken on 26 July 1971 from a distance of 50,000 km, four times the diameter of the Earth.

GLOWING IN THE DARK

Like the other planets of the Solar System, the Earth has also been studied using electromagnetic radiation from parts of the spectrum not visible to human eyes. These studies are revealing details of how the atmosphere works, and are improving our understanding of features such as climatic change and depletion of the ozone layer. This is a far-ultraviolet image, obtained during the Apollo 16 mission, on 21 April 1972. The 10-minute exposure was taken using a filter to block out ultraviolet light from atoms of hydrogen, but allow through light from oxygen and nitrogen, the two main components of our atmosphere. The colour has then been tweaked, as usual, to bring out details of the image. Although the atmosphere glows most brightly on the sunlit side of the Earth, where it is energised by the light from the Sun itself, airglow emission can also be seen on the night side of the planet.

LIFE ON EARTH I

The importance of observations of the Earth from space is highlighted in this dramatic picture, obtained using data from the satellite SeaWiFS (a tortuous acronym derived from Sea-viewing Wide Field-of-view Sensor) in September 1997. Several images have been combined to give a view of the Earth 'unwrapped', as in a conventional map projection. The aim of this was to map the different concentration of marine organisms known as phytoplankton in the world's oceans. The more phytoplankton there are, the greener the water looks. As a bonus, the image also shows the pattern of vegetation across the land surface of the planet; but one of the most striking features is the pall of smoke spreading over south-east Asia, from the forest fires that devastated Indonesia at that time. These fires were started by farmers and forestry workers to clear land, but raged out of control for weeks, producing an environmental catastrophe across the region.

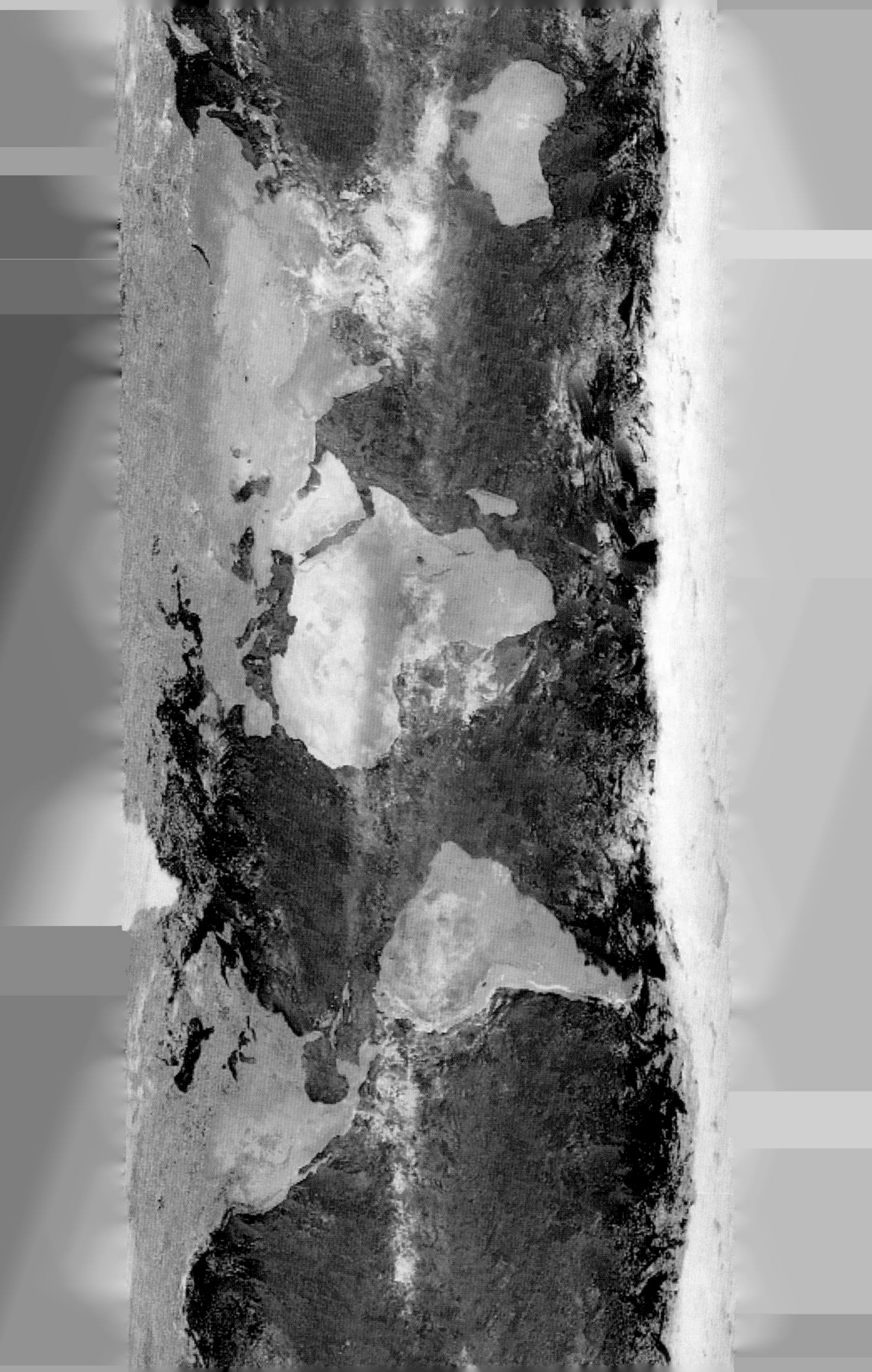

RANGING WITH RADAR

To put the radar-derived images of Venus shown earlier in perspective, here is an example of what the same technology can do when applied to the Earth itself. This image was obtained using a spaceborne radar imaging system carried on board the space shuttle *Endeavour*, on 14 April 1994. It shows a family of dormant volcanoes in the Andes of northern Ecuador, where the city of Otavalo shows up in pink and Lake Otavalo is a black pit inside the triangle formed by the three volcanic peaks. From the top left, reading clockwise, the volcanoes are called Mojanda, Imabura and Cusin. There are lava domes visible on the northern flank of Mojanda, and a lake partly fills the summit crater of this volcano. Mojanda last erupted about 3,400 years ago, but the large volcano visible at the bottom of the picture, Cayambe, was active only 600 years ago. This kind of radar mapping can be used both to study the traces of past eruptions and to help predict future eruptions – if a later mission shows a change in the topography of a volcano, this could be a sign that magma is pushing up from below the crust, ready to burst forth once again.

The region shown in this image is about 50 km from top to bottom of the page, and north is towards the upper right; if you want to find the region in an atlas, it is centres at 0.1°N, 78.1°W. The colours have been assigned arbitrarily to provide technical information about the way the different surface features of the Earth reflect the radar signals.

LIFE ON EARTH II

A global view of the living planet floating in space (compare this with the 'projection' in Plate 58). Plant life in the oceans and on land reflects sunlight in a distinctive way, which can be picked out by the sensors on board satellites. Data from the satellites Nimbus-7 and NOAA-7 have been used to prepare this false-colour image in which areas of dense vegetation on land are coloured green, while the most abundant regions of microscopic plankton in the oceans are coloured red and yellow. Slightly confusingly, this means that yellow regions in the sea denote rich regions for life, whereas yellow regions on land indicate a relative sparsity of plant life. Apart from the beauty of the image, though, its importance is that it clearly shows how far the fertile region of the ocean extends up towards the north pole (the southern ocean is not visible in the picture). This kind of imaging makes it possible to monitor the effects on this essential part of the global food chain of changes in the climate, or of the depletion of ozone at high latitudes being caused by human activities.

THE NOT-SO-PERFECT MOON

When Galileo Galilei first turned his telescope on the Moon in the first decade of the 17th century, he discovered that it is not a perfect sphere with dark and light coloured regions, but is marked by mountains and craters. This perceived imperfection of the Moon was regarded in some circles as heresy, since the Moon was thought to have been created by God, and dogma taught that it had to be a perfect sphere, as a mark of the perfection of God's work. Even in the face of the evidence of their own eyes, some theologians argued that the Moon must 'really' be encased in some invisible substance, like crystal, that did indeed form a perfect sphere, with the mountains and valleys embedded within the crystal. Galileo replied that he had no objection to the hypothesis, provided that he could hypothesise that there might be mountains and valleys of invisible crystal ten times larger than the mountains and valleys visible through his telescope!

This astonishingly crisp image, obtained (appropriately) by the Galileo spaceprobe on 7 December 1992, en route to Jupiter, shows the lumpiness of the Moon in striking detail, especially near the top of the image – the craters there, seen edge-on, look as if something has bitten pieces out of the Moon.

The image is particularly clear because the charge coupled device (CCD) detector carried by Galileo is sensitive not just to visible light, but in part of the infrared region of the spectrum, beyond the range visible to human eyes. Among other details that this highlights, the crater surrounded by bright rays of ejected material at the bottom of the image is the Tycho impact basin.

MAN ON THE MOON

How could we resist it? The classic image of astronaut Edwin 'Buzz' Aldrin, photographed on the surface of the Moon on 20 July 1969, during the Apollo 11 mission. Astronaut Neil Armstrong, who took the picture, carefully set the shot up so that the faceplate of Aldrin's helmet reflects both Armstrong and the Lunar Module in which they had reached the surface. These were the first two human beings to set foot on the surface of the Earth's natural satellite; their footprints, visible on the dusty surface of the Moon, will stay there for thousands of years, because there is no wind to disturb them on the airless Moon.

While Aldrin and Armstrong were making history on the surface of the Moon, the Command Module pilot, Michael Collins, stayed in orbit around the Moon in the Apollo 11 vehicle, waiting for them to return.

THE CRATER COPERNICUS

Galileo would have liked this one. The image was obtained by the Lunar Orbiter 5 spacecraft, in August 1967. It shows the edge of the crater Copernicus, a feature 93 km across that lies within the Mare Imbrium, the dark region of the Moon on the northern part of its visible face. The image shows the flat floor of the crater, a central mound, the crater rim and the rays of material which have sprayed out across its surroundings – the classic features of an impact crater.

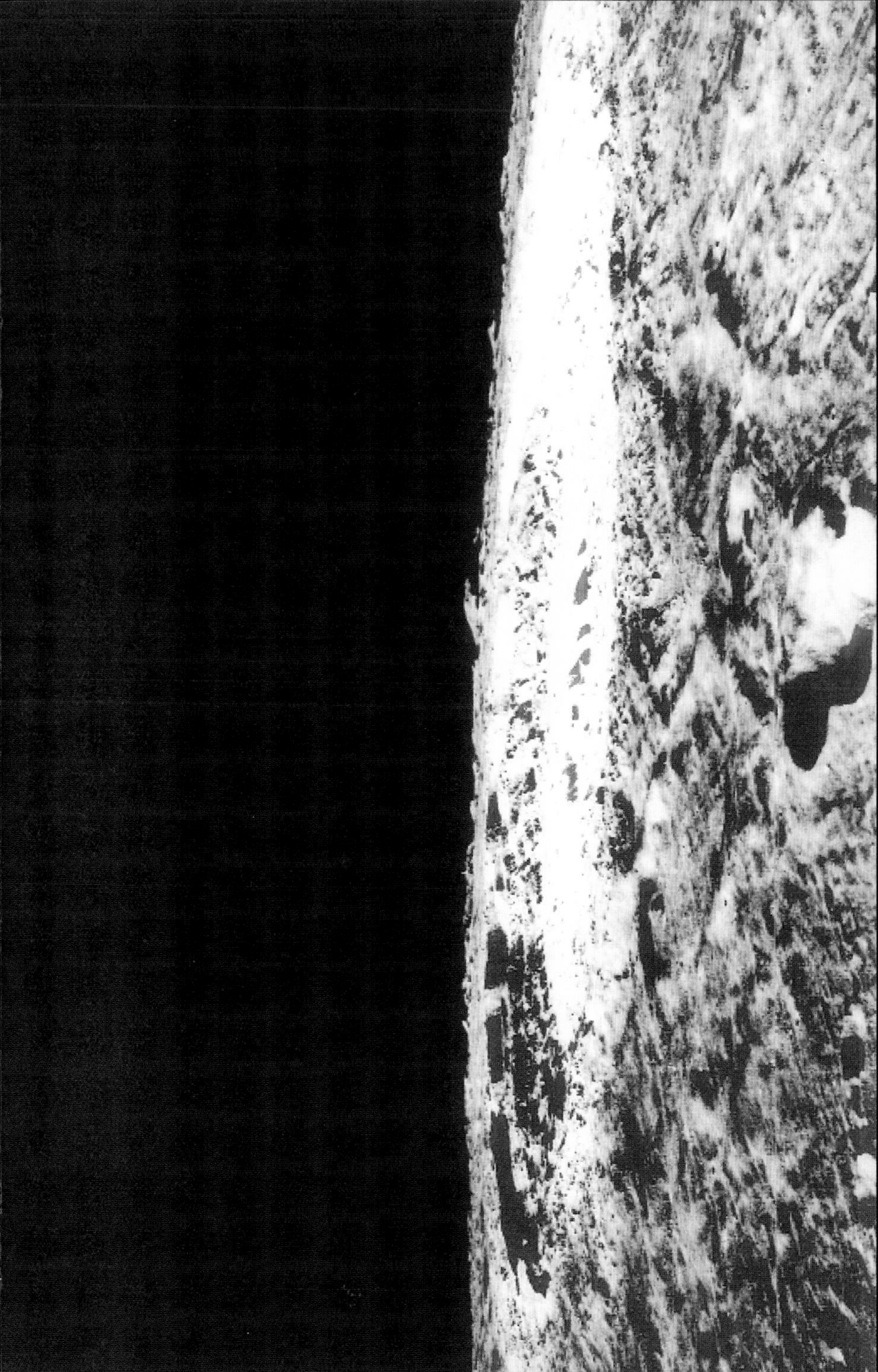

MAKING THE MOST OF THE MOON

The power of modern technology in extracting the maximum amount of information from an image – or set of images – is illustrated in this 'picture' of the Moon, obtained by the Galileo spacecraft on 8 December 1992. At the time the images that went to make up this picture were taken, the probe was 425,000 km from the Moon (and 69,000 km from Earth). It took a series of fifteen separate images of the Moon, using three different filters which each allowed through one colour of light. Different kinds of material reflect different colours of light in different ways, so these images contain information about what the Moon is made of. The information from all these images was then combined to make a mosaic of very nearly the whole Moon (just part of the region at the bottom of the image is missing) and coloured, using the data from the different filters, to give an indication of the composition of the lunar surface material.

Different kinds of rock and dust show up as different colours in this image. Red regions largely correspond to the lunar highlands, while blue and orange colouring correspond to the lava flows of the low-lying mare, bluer mare containing lavas richer in titanium than orange mare. Mare Tranquillitatis is a deep blue patch to the right of the image, and Mare Serenitatis is the smaller, orange circular patch at the upper left of Mare Tranquillitatis. Small purple splotches are deposits produced by explosive volcanic eruptions long ago, and the distinctive crater at the bottom of the image, Tycho, is a feature 85 km across produced by a relatively recent impact.

Galileo actually followed a tortuous route to Jupiter, swinging past Venus once and the Earth twice in order to pick up speed, which is why pictures like this date from the 1990s, even though the probe was launched in 1989 (see also page 151).

THE RED PLANET

This is not a false colour image – Mars really is the Red Planet. Bigger than the Moon, it has enough gravitational pull to cling on to a thin trace of atmosphere. But because there is no life on Mars, and nothing like the kind of strong weathering that occurs in the thicker, wetter atmosphere of Earth, the craters that scar its surface are much more easy to see than those on our home planet. The extent of this ancient cratering shows that the rain of debris that affected the inner planets when the Solar System was young extended all the way out to Mars, whose average distance from the Sun is 1.5 times the average distance of the Earth from the Sun. But, unlike Mercury and the Moon, Mars is also marked by the presence of a handful of huge volcanoes, each bigger than anything on Earth, as well as many smaller volcanic peaks. The largest, Olympus Mons, is 25 km high (three times taller than Mount Everest on Earth) and 600 km in diameter at its base. Because the flanks of the volcano are relatively free from craters, it must be a young feature, in geological terms, which was still erupting as recently as 100 million years ago, when dinosaurs roamed the Earth. Although Olympus Mons is a so-called shield volcano of the same type as the main island of Hawaii, it contains enough material to make a hundred full-size copies of that island.

Volcanic eruptions have changed the appearance of much of the northern hemisphere of Mars, which is also marked by what seem to be channels carved by running water when the planet was young and had a thicker atmosphere (we know these channels are very old, because there are many craters which cut across them). By contrast, the southern hemisphere of Mars is heavily cratered and, like the surfaces of Mercury and the Moon, seems to have changed little since the Solar System was young.

THE FIRST MARTIAN EXPLORER

The tiny Sojourner rover vehicle (about the size of a shoebox) captured the imagination of millions of people when it became the first mobile explorer on the surface of Mars in 1997, as part of the Pathfinder mission. This was the first of a new style of planetary probe, summed up by the slogan 'faster, cheaper, better'. In the case of Pathfinder, 'cheaper' means about $150 million – which, NASA scientists like to point out, compares with the cost of making a blockbuster movie. The next Mars mission, Mars Global Surveyor, went into orbit around the red planet later in 1997, and after manoeuvring gradually into a close orbit around the planet began mapping its surface in detail in 1999.

In this image, taken by the cameras on board the Pathfinder lander which carried Sojourner to Mars, the little rover sits on top of Mermaid Dune, a region of dark material surrounded by brighter Martian surface. The tracks of the rover show as darker red in the foreground. Sojourner operated on the surface for three months (twelve times its design lifetime of seven days) and sent back 550 images; Pathfinder itself (now renamed Sagan Memorial Station, in honour of the late Carl Sagan) operated on the surface for the same period (it was designed to operate for one month) and sent back more than 16,000 images, as well as technical data about conditions on the surface of Mars.

A MARTIAN PANORAMA

This is what Mars would look like if you had eyes in the back of your head, as well as the front. It is a full 360 degree panorama, obtained by the Pathfinder cameras over the course of three consecutive Martian days, in order to ensure the same lighting and shadow conditions for all regions of the surface visible. The Sojourner rover can be seen just to the right of the middle of the picture, nuzzled up against the rock called Yogi, so that its sensors can analyse the chemical composition of the rock. Turn the book sideways so that the pathfinder platform is at the bottom of the page; then, looking more or less towards Sojourner and Yogi, imagine the right and left edges of the image wrapped around in a circle to meet behind your head to get a feel for the all-round view from Pathfinder.

The tracks of Sojourner leading from the ramp by which it reached the surface from Pathfinder, and past the first rock it visited (known as Barnacle Bill) can also be seen.

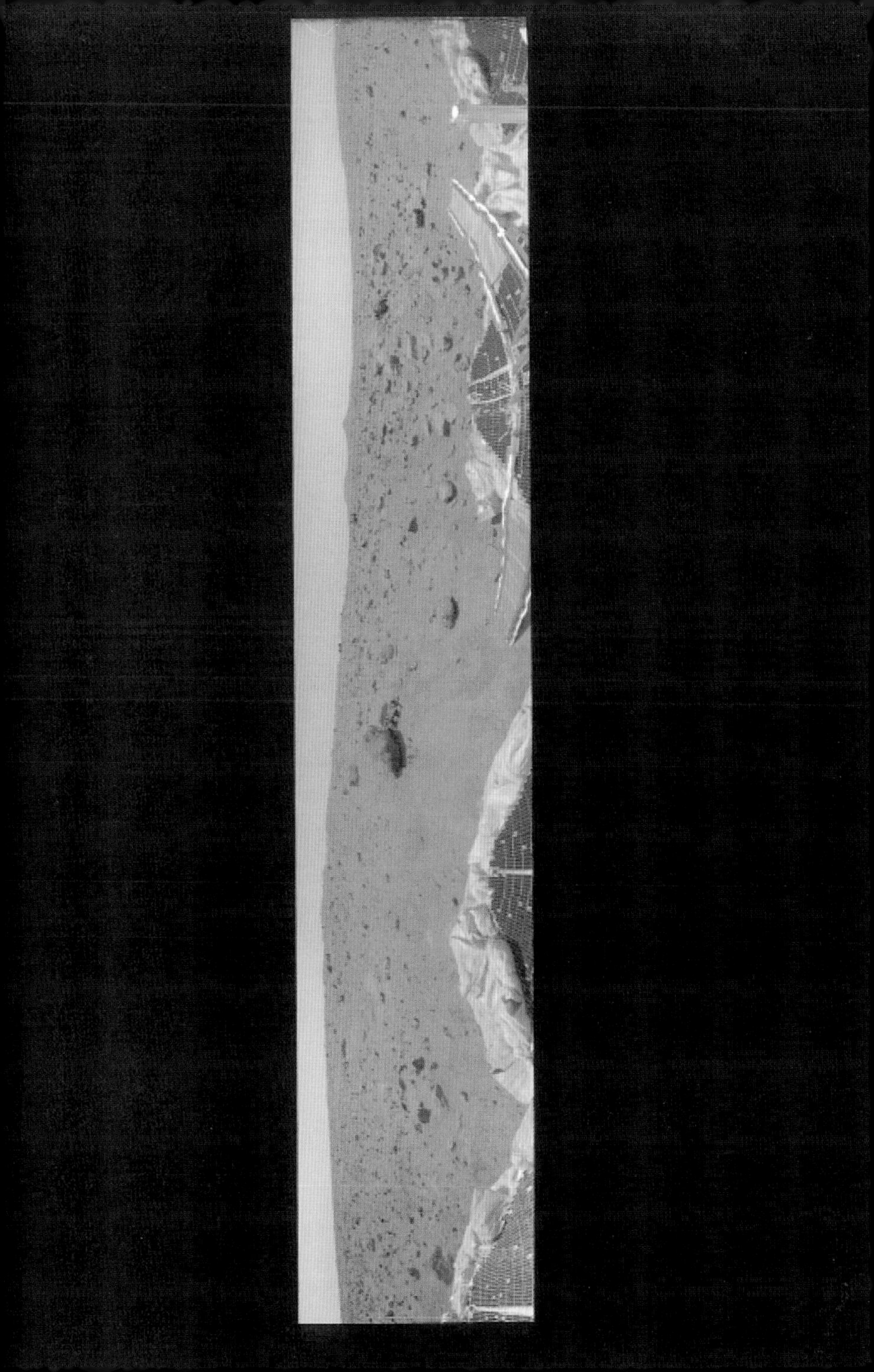

GEOLOGICAL ACTIVITY ON MARS

Although it is now more than twenty years since the Viking probes visited Mars, the wealth of data they sent back to Earth is still providing food for thought. This image, released by NASA only in 1995, was obtained using the standard trick of looking at Mars (from Viking Orbiter cameras) through three different coloured filters, and combining data from the three images to give, in this case, a more or less true-colour view of a region centred on the feature known as Syria Planum. The region is marked by clear signs of geological activity, including volcanoes, and fractures and folds in the rocks caused by movement of the crust. Different regions show up in different colours because of the presence of different amounts of wind-blown sand, and probably because some of the rock itself has changed colour as it has weathered slowly over millions of years.

A MOON OF MARS

Mars has two small moons, Phobos and Deimos. But these are not the same kind of object as our Moon, merely pieces of left-over cosmic rubble that have been captured into orbit around Mars, instead of slamming into its surface. As such, they are typical of the objects that caused the cratering we can still see on the surfaces of Mars and other inner planets today – and in all probability, very similar to the object that smashed into the Earth 65 million years ago and brought an end to the era of the dinosaurs.

There are few pictures of the moons of Mars from close up, but in 1971 the Mariner 9 spaceprobe passed by Phobos and took this picture, from a distance of 2,140 km. It is clear from this image that Phobos itself has been battered by many collisions with smaller objects during its lifetime. The orbit of Phobos is unstable, and slowly decaying; in about 30 million years from now it too will smash into the surface of Mars, adding a rather impressive crater to the markings on the surface of the Red Planet.

Phobos measures roughly 27 by 21 by 19 km, and orbits Mars once every 7 hours 40 minutes at a distance of 9,380 km. Because this is faster than the rate at which Mars rotates (the length of one day of Mars is just 40 minutes longer than the length of one day on Earth), from the surface of Mars Phobos is seen to move backwards across the sky, rising in the west and setting in the east.

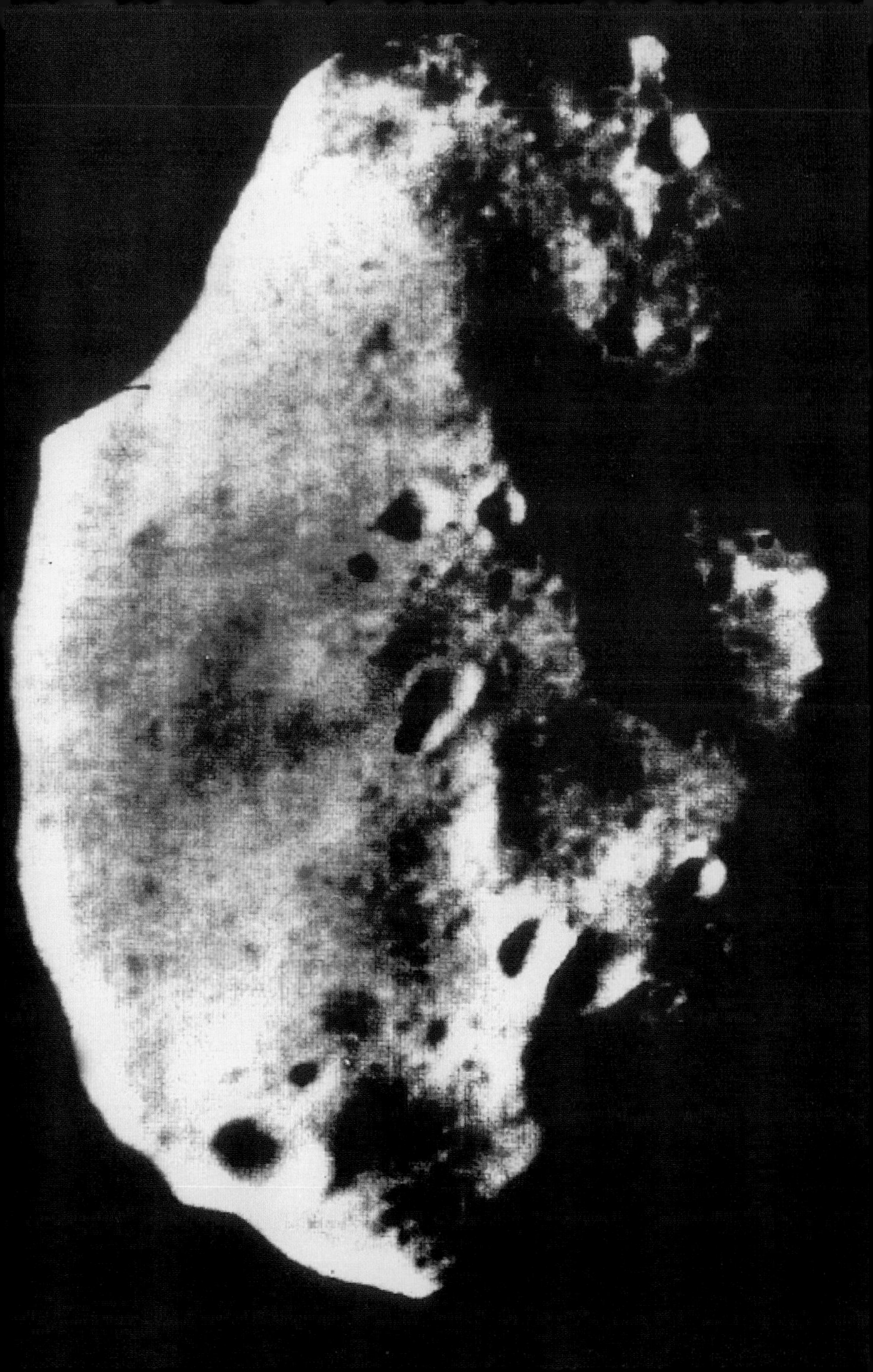

ASTEROID GASPRA

Even a glance at this image of asteroid 951 Gaspra, obtained on 29 October 1991 by the Galileo spacecraft on its way to Jupiter, shows that it bears a striking similarity to Phobos (Plate 69). Gaspra is a typical member of the belt of asteroids that lies between the orbits of Mars and Jupiter, and is also typical of the kind of cosmic rubble that pounded the inner planets when the Solar System was young. It is 19 by 12 by 11 km in size (slightly smaller than Phobos); the region illuminated by sunlight (shining from the left of the picture) in this image measures about 18 km from upper left to lower right.

This image is a masterpiece of data processing, produced using all the best data from Galileo. The basic image is a high-resolution black-and-white photograph of the asteroid, but colour information obtained by viewing the asteroid through three different filters in turn has been added as well. To the naked eye, the subtle variations in colour of the asteroid would not be noticeable; here, the contrast has been exaggerated slightly and false colour used to highlight the different regions of the surface of Gaspra. Blue areas are more reflective, and also show absorption of light at wavelengths typical of absorption by the mineral olivine, a semi-precious stone here on Earth. These regions tend to be along the ridges of Gaspra, and associated with some of the more sharply defined (and therefore, presumably, younger) craters. Slightly reddish regions are associated with relatively low-lying parts of the asteroid's surface, and are less reflective. The explanation for these differences is that underlying rock has been exposed in the bluer regions, while dusty debris has accumulated in the redder regions.

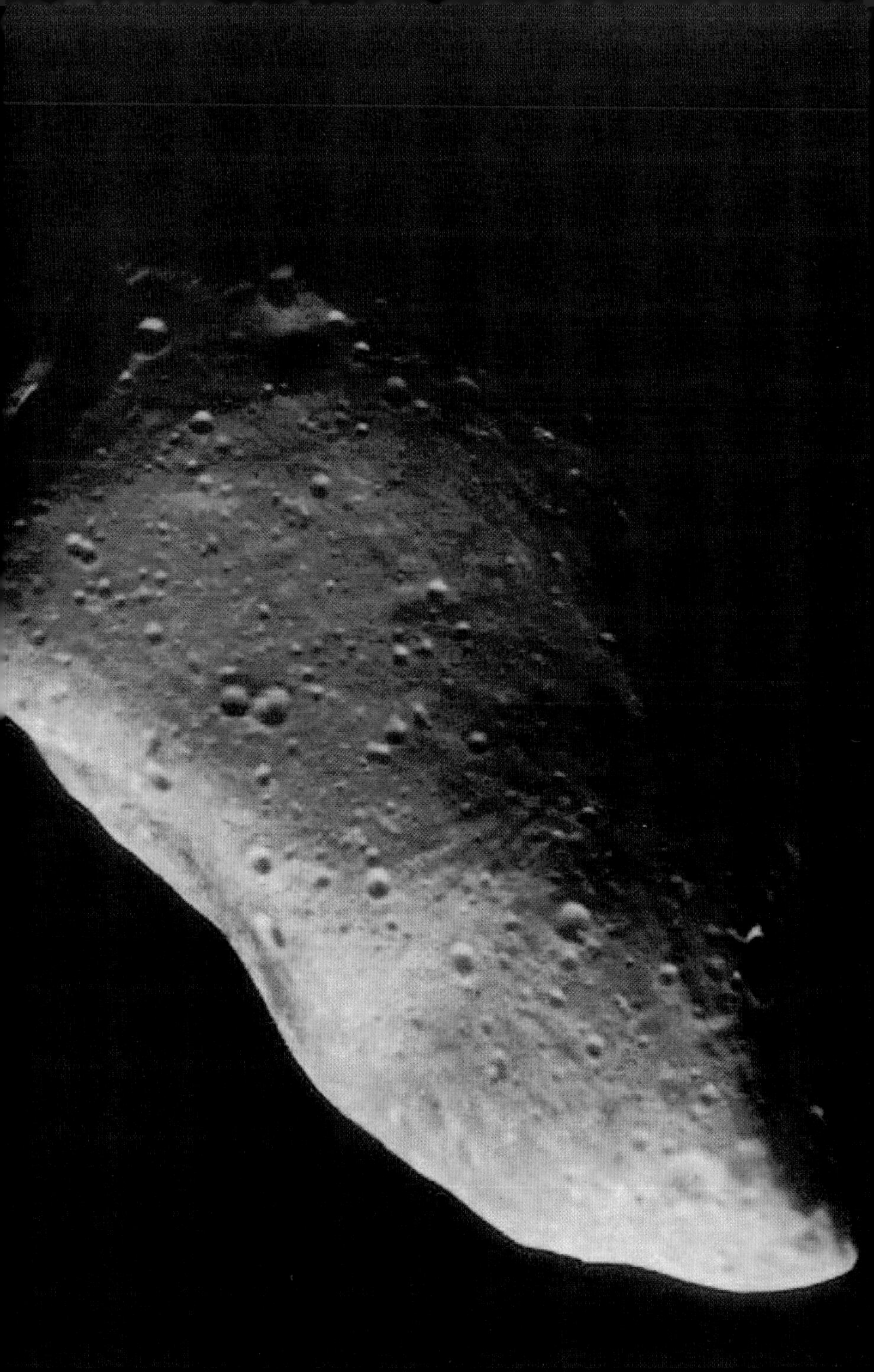

A COMETARY STRING OF PEARLS

Although most comets orbit the Sun far away in the Oort Cloud, we become aware of them only when they fall in towards the Sun, crossing the orbit of Jupiter and getting hot enough to produce a glowing tail of gas that streams out behind them (see page 169). The most spectacular of these visitors in recent times in astronomical terms (although it was never visible to the naked eye from Earth) was the comet discovered by Carolyn and Gene Shoemaker and David Levy in March 1993. Since it was the ninth comet discovered by the team, it is officially known as Shoemaker-Levy 9; but to everyone it is the Shoemaker-Levy comet. It passed by Jupiter so close that the icy ball of material at the nucleus of the comet was torn apart by the gravity of the giant planet into a 'string of pearls', twenty-one of which are visible in this picture, obtained by the Wide Field Planetary Camera on the Hubble Space Telescope. The length of the string of pearls pictured here is 1.1 million km, three times the distance from the Earth to the Moon. The largest of the cometary fragments in the string were between 2 and 4 km across. The whole string of cometary debris orbited Jupiter a few times, and then crashed into the planet in a series of spectacular impacts in July 1994.

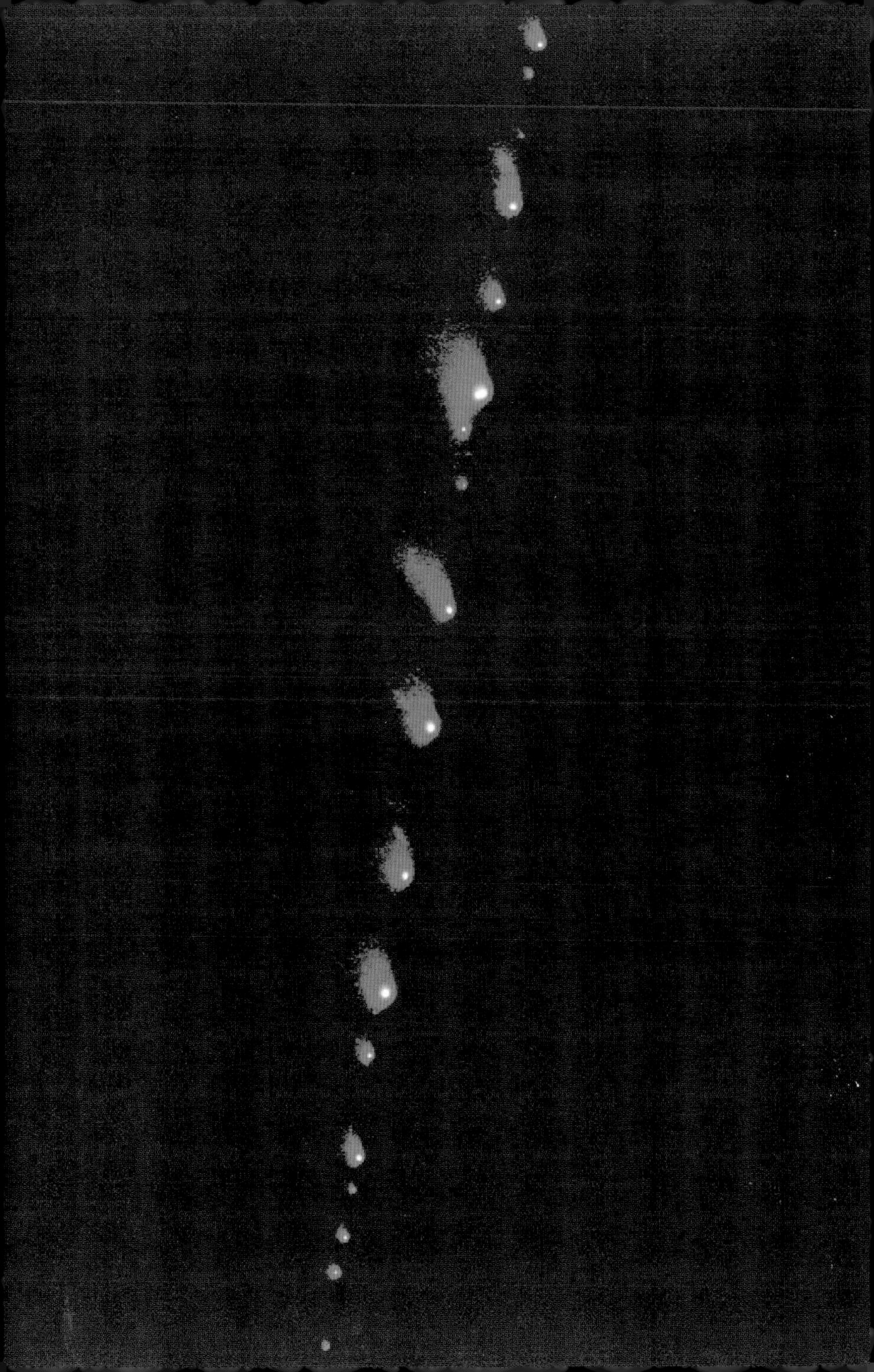

THE HEART OF A COMET

The closest view of the heart of a comet yet obtained was captured by the spaceprobe Giotto, which flew past the nucleus of Halley's Comet in March 1986, during the most recent passage of the comet through the inner Solar System. Although the probe approached to within 596 km of the nucleus of the comet, sending back scientific data all the time, its cameras were knocked out by an impact with a small piece of cometary material soon after this picture was taken, from a distance of 6,500 km, 95 seconds before closest approach.

The images and other data sent back show that, as expected, the nucleus is a lump of icy material, with 80 per cent of its mass in the form of water-ice. But most astronomers were surprised by observations which suggest that there are large lumps of rock embedded in the ice – not a flying snowball, but an icy rock pile. They were also surprised at how dark the surface is (the dark nucleus is just visible in the upper left of the picture; the bright stuff we see here is gas streaming out and away from the nucleus). The nucleus is an irregularly shaped object, roughly 16 by 8 by 8 km, about the size of the island of Manhattan. Its surface is literally blacker than coal, and reflects less than 4 per cent of the light that falls upon it. This makes the nucleus very hard to see, even with the best telescopes, and because they had assumed it must be more reflective than this, astronomers had calculated that the nucleus was smaller than Giotto revealed it to be. The black surface (which is rich in carbon compounds) is now explained as a crusty layer of dusty material that forms each time the comet passes close by the Sun (Halley's Comet comes in as close as 0.6 AU to the Sun, closer than Venus does). The heat of the Sun makes the comet active, and the gas jetting out from cracks in its surface (as we see in this image overleaf) carries dust with it. But when the comet is far away from the Sun at the other end of its orbit (which, in the case of Halley's Comet, is at 35 AU, beyond the orbit of Neptune), the black dust settles back down over the surface. It is very likely that other cometary nuclei are equally dark and unreflective, and that their sizes have been underestimated in the same way.

THE GIANT PLANET

Jupiter is by far the largest planet in the Solar System, so large that Earth would fit into Jupiter just over 1,400 times. Jupiter actually contains 70 per cent of the mass of all the planets put together. Jupiter is the first of the gas giant planets, which are made up almost entirely of hydrogen and helium (as the Sun is) and do not have solid surfaces like the Earth and other terrestrial planets.

Such a massive planet dominates the Solar System and, it has been argued, helps to protect life on Earth. The planet acts as a giant cosmic vacuum cleaner, capturing many comets and asteroids before they enter the inner Solar System and preventing them from hitting Earth. One of these captures was seen recently as Comet Shoemaker-Levy collided with Jupiter.

Jupiter is thought to be the cause of the asteroid belt as well. Its powerful gravitational field is thought to have pulled and pushed rocks in the asteroid belt, preventing them from joining together and forming a planet. What we now see there is the remaining debris from a failed planet.

Jupiter is so large that it has its own mini 'solar system', in particular the four giant Galilean satellites (three of which are larger than the Moon) and twelve other known satellites, many of which are little more than captured asteroids. This picture from Voyager 1 shows the two most interesting Galilean moons – Io and Europa, about which we have much more to say – as they cross the face of Jupiter. Io (on the left) is passing by the Great Red Spot, a huge storm in Jupiter's atmosphere.

TWO VIEWS OF EUROPA

This double image (overleaf) of one of the moons of Jupiter, Europa, provides a stunning example of the detail available in the pictures sent back to Earth by the Galileo probe. By showing the same image twice in slightly different fashions, we can also indicate the effects of the kind of false-colour treatment that is commonly used to highlight features of particular scientific interest.

If you look at the images side by side, the view on the left is a close approximation to the natural colour of Europa, as it would appear to the unaided human eye. The image on the right is a colour-enhanced version which brings out even more clearly the differences between the different materials that make up the crust of the moon. Europa is essentially a smooth ball of ice (the smoothest object known in the Solar System), with rock embedded in it. The dark brown regions are rocky material, some of which may have come from within Europa, and some of which may have arrived in the form of asteroids crashing in to the moon. The bright plains in the polar regions at the top and bottom of the right-hand image are coded in shades of blue to distinguish regions of coarse-grained ice (dark blue) from regions covered by finer-grained ice (light blue). The incredibly fine lines, only 20-40 km wide, and running like veins through the ice, are fractures in the surface, some of them more than 3,000 km long, like the fractures that might be produced by hitting a glass marble with a small hammer – but nobody is sure what caused them to form. Evidence that Europa does get struck by blows from space can be seen in the lower right of the image, where there is a young impact crater about 50 km across. The most likely explanation for the lack of craters across most of the surface is that liquid water has seeped out from the interior and filled in the craters with ice, but the presence of some surface features suggests that at least part of the surface has been stable for at least 10 million years. Most of the surface is probably younger than that – possibly much younger (see the caption to Plate 76).

The image was obtained by Galileo on 7 September 1996, from a distance of 677,000 km (a little less than twice the distance from the Earth to the Moon). Europa is 3,139 km in diameter, slightly smaller than our own Moon. It takes just over 3.5 days to orbit Jupiter.

EUROPA IN CLOSE-UP

This false-colour image shows a region of Europa known as Minos Linea in more detail. It was obtained by the Galileo spaceprobe on 28 June 1996. The area covered by this image is about 1,260 km from top to bottom of the page, and the smallest features resolved by the imaging system on board Galileo are less than 2 km across. The vein-like cracks in the ice seem to be filled with material that has seeped into them from below the icy surface of the moon. Europa almost certainly has a rocky core below its ice-covered surface, with liquid water present at least part of the time in the boundary between them; it is probably heated in its interior by the tides raised in the solid rock by Jupiter, constantly flexing the core.

The visible surface is a cracked layer of ice lying on top of the liquid water, which is heated from below in a manner reminiscent of the way underwater volcanic activity on Earth warms the deep ocean. On Earth, the heat and chemicals from this volcanic activity have acted as a kind of geological incubator, giving rise to weird life forms that never see the Sun; it is just possible that something similar may exist in the depths of the oceans of Europa, far beneath the visible crust.

Close-up images obtained by the Galileo probe in April 1997 and December 1997 (see Plate 76) suggest that much of the icy surface is much younger and thinner than had previously been suspected; the images show icebergs and flat blocks of ice jostling together, just like the icy debris seen on the polar seas of the Earth during the spring thaw of the polar sea ice.

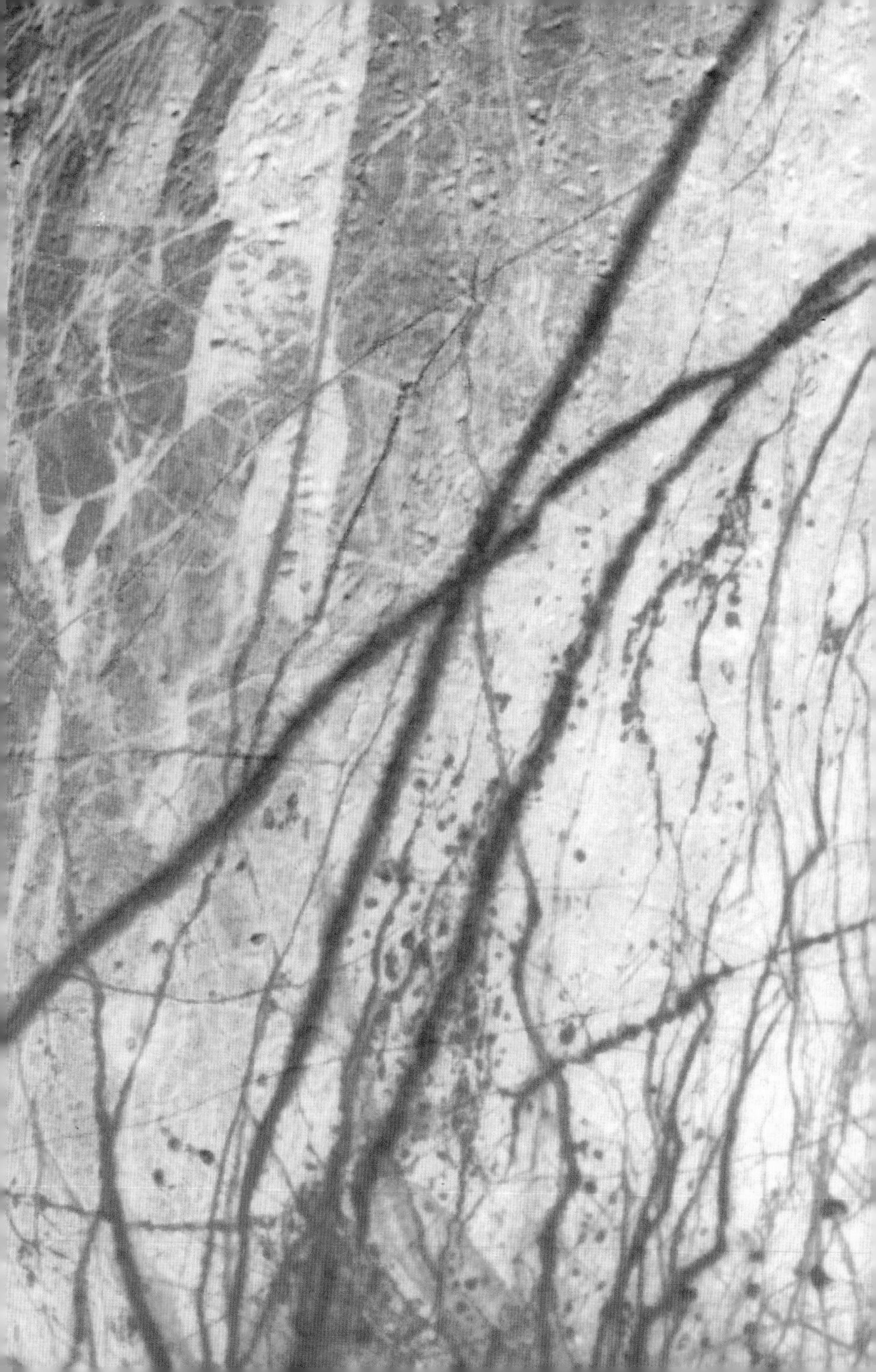

EUROPE: EXTREME CLOSE-UP

The Galileo spaceprobe proved so durable and successful that after completing its two-year primary mission of exploration of the Jupiter system, it was sent on another tour of the Jovian moons, which lasted until 1999. One of the first objectives of this extended mission was to obtain an extreme close-up view of Europa on a close pass over the surface of the moon, which took place on 16 December 1997. This image was obtained during that flyby, at a distance of just 200 km above the frozen surface. It provides the clearest evidence yet that the visible surface of Europa is only an icy crust covering an ocean of liquid water. There are now plans to send a submersible probe to Europa some time this century, to penetrate the ice and search for signs of life in the ocean below.

By the end of 1997, Galileo had sent back a gigabyte of data and 1,800 images, including hundreds of close-up pictures of Jupiter's moons, to Earth; Galileo flew past Europa a further seven times as well as revisiting Callisto and Io.

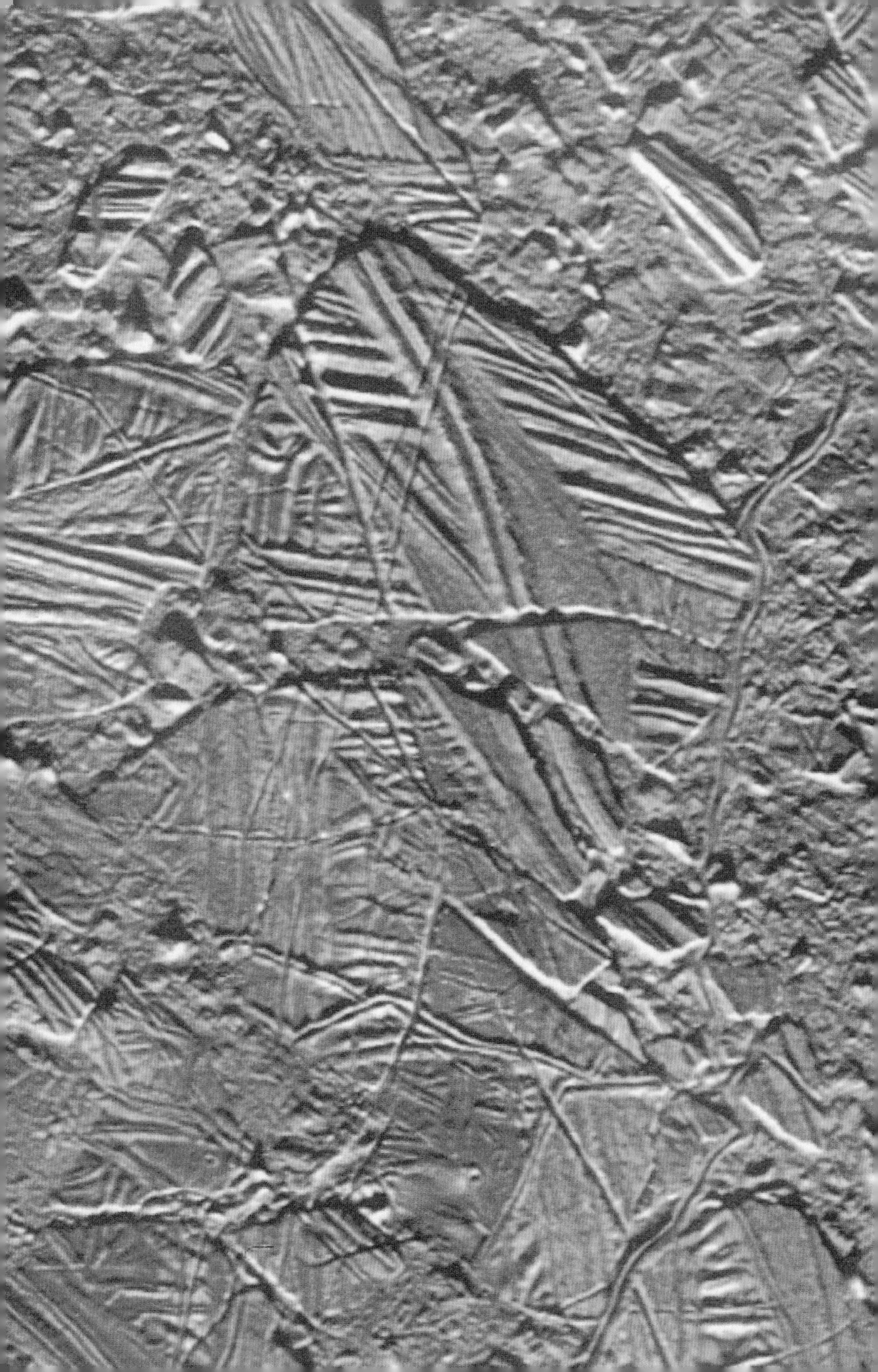

IO, THE VOLCANIC MOON

In the whole of the story of the exploration of the Solar System to date, perhaps the biggest surprise came when the Voyager probes found active volcanoes on Io, the innermost of the four large moons that orbit Jupiter. It is now clear that Io is the most volcanically active body in the entire Solar System.

Io orbits so close to Jupiter (at a distance of only 422,000 km, almost as close as the Moon is to Earth) that the tidal pull of the giant planet squeezes the moon rhythmically, generating heat in its interior. It is this internal heat that drives the volcanic activity. The material spewed out from the interior of the moon by this activity is rich in sodium, which forms a cloud around the moon; but the spectacular coloration of the surface shown overleaf is caused by the presence of sulphur and sulphur compounds laid down on the surface by the volcanism.

The image, from the Galileo spaceprobe, was obtained by adding colour data obtained through three different filters on 7 September 1996 to a high-resolution black-and-white image obtained on 6 November 1996. The colours are essentially natural, but have been slightly enhanced to emphasise the contrast between different regions of the surface. The colour data were obtained when the spaceprobe was 487,000 km from Io, and the high-resolution data from a series of pictures taken at distances ranging from 245,719 km to 403,000 km.

The smallest features visible in this combined image are about 2.5 km across. Among the many striking details in this picture, just above the centre is a volcano pouring out a black trail of ejected material, while just below this another volcano has spewed reddish sulphurous material out across the surface.

Io has a diameter of 3,630 km (comparable to our Moon's 3,476 km) and a mass 20 per cent greater than that of our Moon, showing that it is composed largely of rock. Like our Moon, it is locked in an orbit with one side always facing towards its parent planet; this view is of the side that is always turned away from Jupiter.

THE OTHER GALILEAN SATELLITES

As well as the imperfections on the surface of the Moon, one of the first discoveries made by Galileo when he turned his telescope towards the heavens at the beginning of the 17th century was that Jupiter is circled by four large moons. These are now known as the Galilean satellites of Jupiter. The image of Jupiter circled by its moons was instrumental in helping to establish the idea that the planets, including the Earth, circle the Sun in the same way; the Jovian system was, and is, perceived as a kind of miniature solar system. It is now known that Jupiter has a family of at least 16 moons (as well as the faint ring system), making the resemblance to the Solar System even more striking. But the four Galilean satellites are by far the biggest and most important of these – some of the lesser moons, like the two moons of Mars, are probably simply captured pieces of cosmic junk.

We have already looked at two of the Galilean satellites, Europa and Io. Here are the other two (overleaf): Ganymede is on the left, with Callisto on the right. In order of their distances from Jupiter, Io is closest, followed by Europa, Ganymede and Callisto. Ganymede is the largest (indeed, the largest moon in the Solar System, and bigger than Mercury), with a diameter of 5,262 km; it has a very low density, less than twice that of water, and is mainly made of ice. Callisto has a similarly low density, and is also largely made of ice, and is a little smaller than Ganymede, with a diameter of 4,800 km (almost exactly the same size as Mercury). The two moons shown here are less active than the two inner Galilean satellites, because they are further from Jupiter and subjected to lower tidal stresses.

However, there has been some internal activity on Ganymede, which has partially resurfaced the moon since it formed. Callisto, even further from Jupiter, shows no sign of internal activity, and seems to have retained its primordial surface, which is now completely smothered by craters caused by impacts long ago. This, and other evidence, suggests that the Galilean moons formed in orbit around Jupiter from a disk of primordial material, in much the same way that the planets formed in orbit around the Sun.

THE GREAT RED SPOT

No picture sequence of the Jovian system would be complete without a close-up of the Great Red Spot. The spot is essentially a huge weather system in the atmosphere of Jupiter, equivalent to the high-pressure systems (anticyclones) that drift across the surface of the Earth. But this anticyclone is three times the size of the entire Earth, and the winds around it have been blowing for at least three centuries – it was first observed by Robert Hooke, in 1664.

This image was obtained by the spaceprobe Voyager 2, on 6 July 1979, from a range of 2,633,003 km.

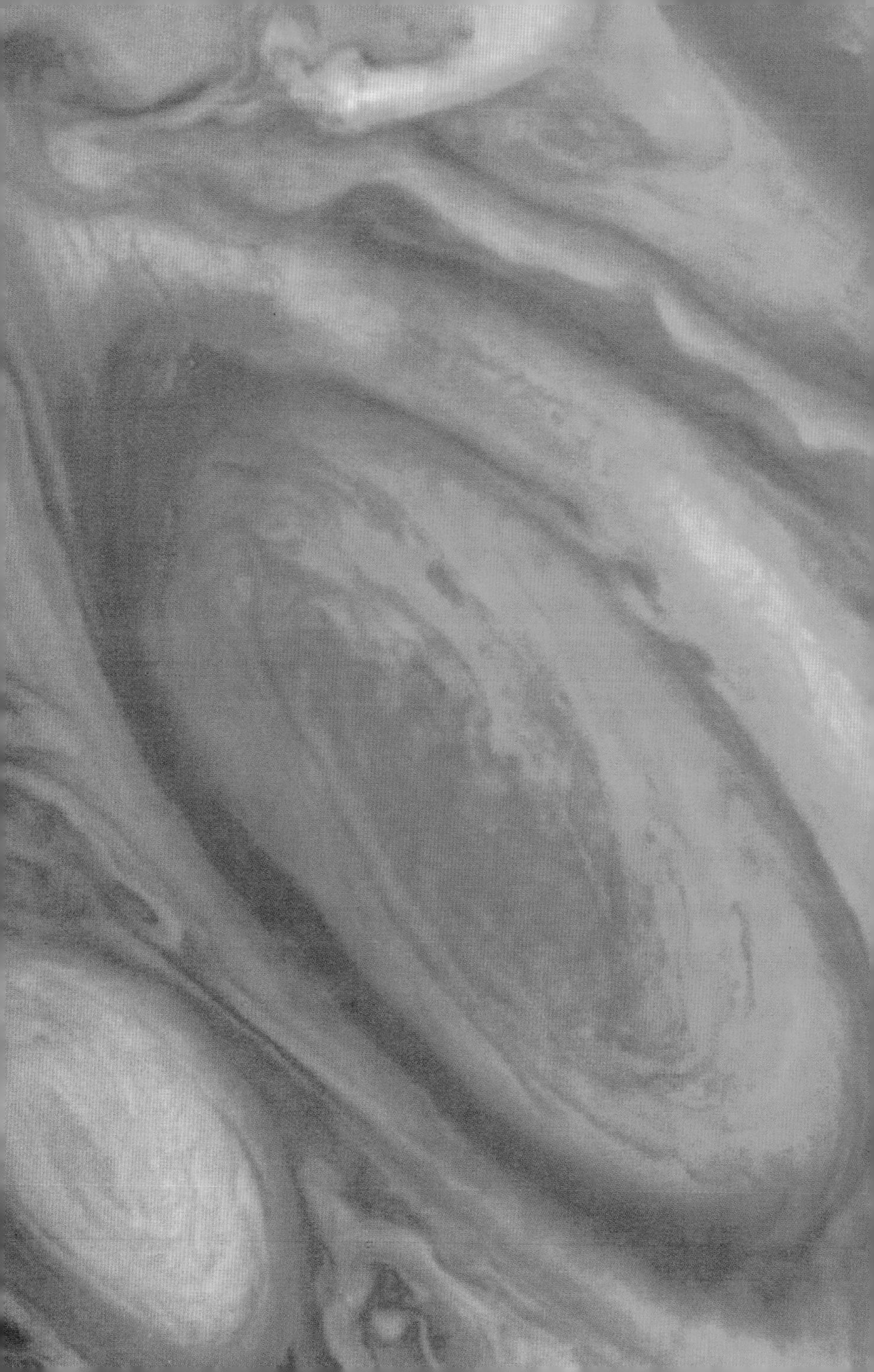

THE RINGS OF SATURN

Although Galileo, with the aid of his astronomical telescope, could see that there was something peculiar about the planet Saturn, which seemed to have a bulge on either side, it was only in the late 1650s that the Dutch astronomer Christiaan Huygens, using an improved telescope that he built with his brother Constantijn, discovered that Saturn is surrounded by a thin, flat ring, with a clear gap between the ring and the planet. Later observations, by Giovanni Cassini in 1675, showed that there is a gap in the rings, still known as the Cassini Division. But the true nature of the rings was not understood until 1859, when the Scottish physicist James Clerk Maxwell, in one of his earliest scientific papers, proved that the rings could not be solid objects, because if they were they would be torn apart by tidal forces; they must be made up of a myriad of tiny particles, each one in its own orbit around Saturn, like a tiny moon.

The fine structure of the rings is clearly brought out in images like this one, obtained by the spaceprobe Voyager 1 on 13 November 1980, looking back at Saturn from a distance of 1,500,000 km beyond the ringed planet on its journey out of the Solar System. The image was exposed to bring out the detail in the rings. The appearance of the ring system is reminiscent of the grooves in a vinyl record, but each groove is made up of many tiny moonlets following essentially the same orbit around Saturn.

It was Maxwell who invented the technique of making colour images by using information from three black-and-white photographs taken through three different coloured filters. Images like this one, obtained using the photographic technique invented by Maxwell, confirm the structure of the rings predicted by Maxwell more than a hundred years earlier.

THE RINGED PLANET

This enhanced colour image of Saturn shows the distinctly flattened shape of the ringed planet. Saturn is nearly ten times bigger across than the Earth, and has a diameter of 120,660 km at its equator (it is the second largest planet in the Solar System, after Jupiter), but it spins so rapidly (the day on Saturn lasts just 10 hours 14 minutes) that centrifugal force makes it bulge at the equator so much that it is 10 per cent smaller measured pole to pole. The outermost part of the ring system visible here has a diameter of 272,400 km – but the rings are only about 100 m thick, incredibly thin in proportion to their diameter. The two main rings, picked out by Cassini more than 300 years ago, are known as the A ring (on the outside) and the B ring (the inner ring), separated by the Cassini Division, a gap 3,500 km across, almost as wide as the United States measured from the Pacific to the Atlantic coasts.

This image was obtained by one of the Voyager craft, but the record of which of the two Voyager probes it was, the exact date and the distance of the probe from Saturn have been lost in the NASA archive. Three of the moons of Saturn (Tethys, Dione and Rhea) can be seen against the black backdrop of space, and a fourth, Mimas, is visible passing in front of Saturn, on the right-hand side of the image just below the rings, Saturn has at least twenty moons, with more still being discovered (not counting the huge number of tiny moonlets that make up the rings).

A BLACK-AND-WHITE MOON

The moons of Saturn are as distinctive and strange as the moons of Jupiter. When investigated by spaceprobes for the first time, as for the moons of Jupiter they turned out to be nothing like the way astronomers had imagined them on the basis of the limited information available from ground-based telescopes. Iapetus, pictured here, is the outermost large moon of Saturn, and one of the most peculiar objects in the Solar System. It orbits Saturn once every 79 days at an average distance of 3,560,000 km (far outside the ring system), and has a diameter of 1,600 km. Nothing very peculiar about that; but one side of the moon (the hemisphere that leads in the direction of the moon's orbital motion around Saturn) is a dark black colour, as if it were covered by material like tar or asphalt. It reflects so little that the cameras on board Voyager 2 could pick out no details of the terrain. The other side of Iapetus, shown here, is brightly reflective and seems to be made of dirty ice and snow, with many large impact craters scarring its surface. Nobody knows why the two hemispheres should be so different.

This image was obtained on 22 August 1981, by Voyager 2. The smallest features visible are about 15 km across; no finer details are visible because Voyager 2 never went closer to Iapetus than about a million kilometres (more than twice the distance from the Earth to the Moon). This enigmatic moon was one of the primary targets for the Cassini mission which arrived at the Saturn system in 2004.

ANOTHER HOME FOR LIFE?

At first sight, the image overleaf is the least exciting in the book. But it shows us one of the most interesting and potentially exciting places in the Solar System: Titan, the most likely place to find life outside the Earth. Titan, the largest moon of Saturn, orbits its parent planet at a distance of 1,222,000 km, once every 15 days. It has a diameter of 5,150 km and a thick atmosphere (so thick that the pressure at the surface is one and a half times the pressure of the air at the surface of the Earth), mainly composed of nitrogen but laced with methane and ammonia, and shrouded (as shown in this image) by orange clouds which contain complex organic molecules produced by the activity of lightning in the chemical soup of the atmosphere.

Don't be fooled by the word 'organic', though; to a chemist, organic molecules are complex compounds containing carbon. They are indeed important to life forms like ourselves, which are carbon-based, but they are not on their own proof of the existence of life. Nevertheless, it is thought that very similar conditions to those that exist on Titan today (nitrogen, methane, ammonia and the effects of lightning) existed on the Earth when the Solar System was young, and may have led to the emergence of living molecules.

On Earth, there were oceans of liquid water in which the complex chemistry of life could emerge. Titan, much farther from the Sun, is a frozen moon, with a surface temperature of minus 180 degrees Celsius, and all its water locked up in ice, so the complex molecules that may be the precursors of life remain as an orange haze in the atmosphere. Radar pulses bounced off Titan in the late 1980s suggest that there may be a partially liquid surface, perhaps a slushy ocean of liquid methane and frozen water.

In a few billions of years from now, when the Sun nears the end of its life, it will swell up to become what is known as a red giant star. The extra heat from the ageing star will incinerate the inner planets of the Solar System, but may bring Titan to life, as it emerges from deep freeze and perhaps passes through the same sequence of events that led to the emergence of life on Earth. In the much closer future, investigations of Titan may provide information about what the Earth was like when it was young, and how life got started in our home planet. The next step in this investigation will come when the Cassini craft drops a small probe, known as Huygens, into the atmosphere of Titan.

ANOTHER BATTERED MOON

Totally unlike either Iapetus or Titan, Tethys, another of the moons of Saturn, shows a battered face reminiscent of the cratering that scars the surface of Mercury – another example of the similarity between the way in which the larger moons formed in orbit around the giant planets and the way in which the planets themselves formed in orbit around the Sun. This image, obtained by Voyager 2, clearly shows a particularly large (and relatively recent) impact crater in the upper right, near a wide trench that stretches diagonally across the ice-covered surface of the moon. Tethys orbits Saturn once every 45 hours, at a distance of 294,670 km. It has a diameter of 1,060 km.

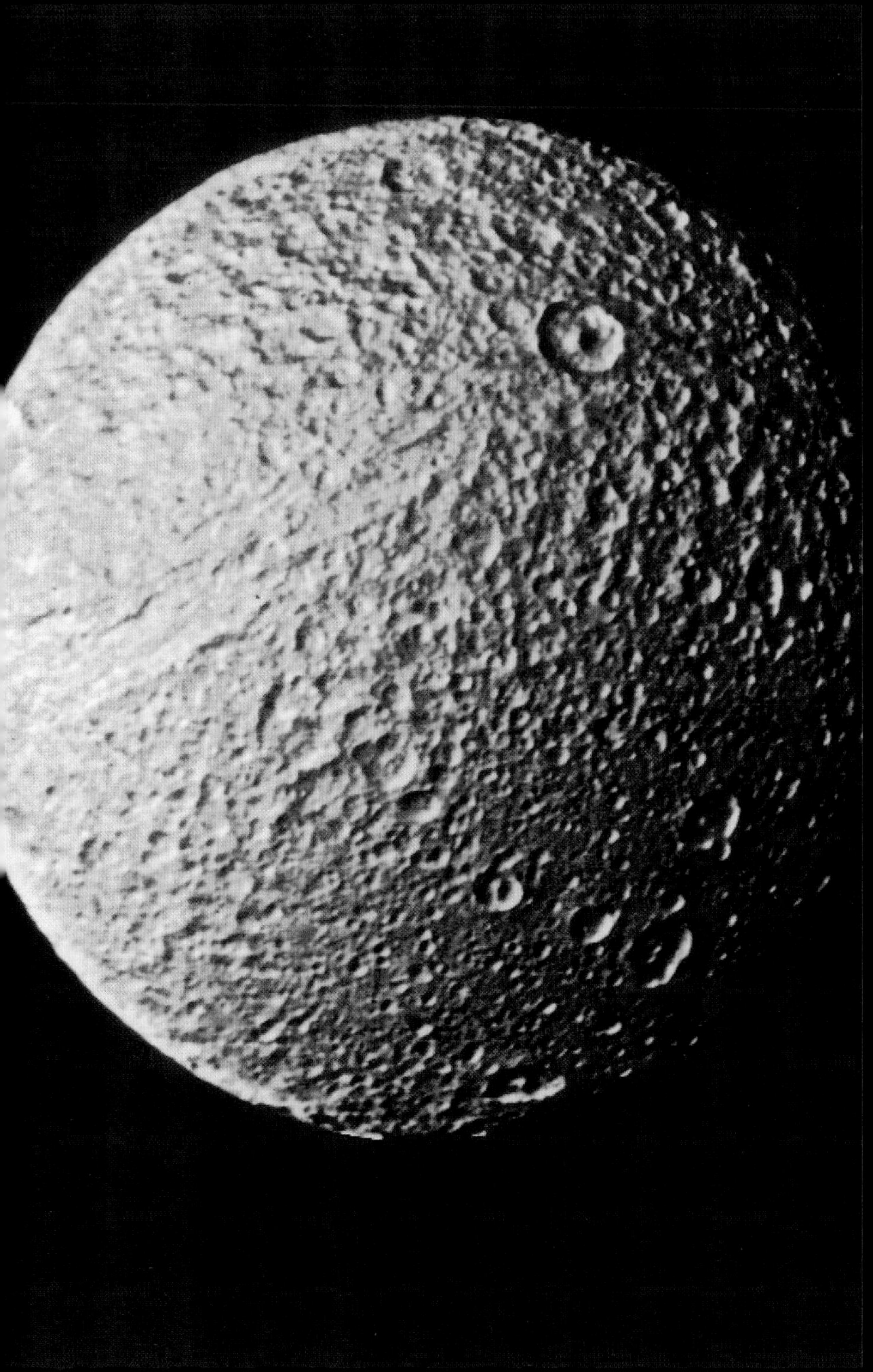

THE CLOUDS OF SATURN

Whereas the image in Plate 80 was exposed to bring out detail in the rings of Saturn, the rings are scarcely visible in this image, which has been processed to emphasise the coloured bands and other features formed in the clouds of Saturn itself. As well as the coloured bands, you can see spots which are thought to be similar to (but much bigger than) thunderstorms on Earth. The image makes no pretence of representing the true colours of Saturn – the violet-coloured belt of clouds would actually look brown to the human eye – but it is a spectacular image of a fascinating planet.

The picture is based on data obtained by Voyager 1 on 18 October 1980, using three different coloured filters. The edge of the ring system at the lower right has been clipped off by the cameras on board Voyager 1, which were not quite perfectly centred on Saturn.

SATURN: A FAMILY PORTRAIT

This family portrait of the Saturnian system was put together by the Voyager project team using images obtained by Voyager 1 during November 1980. The montage shows the moon Dione in the foreground. Saturn and its rings behind Dione, the moons Tethys and Mimas in the distance to the upper right, Enceladus and Rhea at the lower left, and orange Titan far away at the top. This is like an artist's impression, of course; you could never see the Saturnian system looking just like this is real life, though every image is a genuine Voyager 1 photograph.

URANUS: A FAMILY PORTRAIT

In 1986, the Voyager spacecraft found ten previously unknown moons of Uranus, and in 1997 two more small moons, orbiting a long way out from the planet, were discovered by astronomers using the ground-based Hale Telescope on Mount Palomar. This brought the total number of Uranian moons known at the end of 1997 to seventeen (by 2006 that number had risen to 27). The 'new' moons are 160 km across and 80 km in diameter; they orbit at about 8 million km and 6 million km, respectively, from Uranus.

Uranus itself is visually one of the most boring objects in the Solar System – a featureless blue sphere. This image is a montage put together by NASA's Jet Propulsion Laboratory from two images obtained by Voyager 2, with the thin line of the Uranian ring system added by an artist. It shows the view of the giant planet as it might appear rising over the horizon of its moon Miranda.

MIRANDA: A MYSTERIOUS MOON

The smallest (just under 500 km across) and innermost of the five largest moons of Uranus, Miranda has a geologically complex surface which seems to have resulted from the moon being smashed apart by a major impact, and the pieces then gradually drifting back together under the pull of their own gravity. The process may even have happened more than once. One result of this turbulent history is that the most striking feature on the surface of Miranda is a fault valley 15 km deep, which gives the jagged edge to the bottom right of the moon's surface in this Voyager 2 image. This bizarre history of the moon may be related to the bizarre nature of the Uranian system as a whole. Unlike the other planets in the Solar System, which orbit upright as they circle around the Sun, Uranus orbits on its side, with first one pole and then the other pointing towards the Sun as it follows its own 84-year orbit. Uranus's moons and rings follow circular orbits around the equator of the planet, making the whole system like a bull's-eye target at right angles to the plane in which all the planets (including Uranus) orbit the Sun. It may be that this is the result of a massive impact by some object with Uranus long ago, which literally knocked the planet on its side and created the present system of moons around Uranus from the resulting debris.

Because the moons were spread out in this bull's-eye pattern at right angles to the trajectory of Voyager 2, the probe was able to make a close pass by only one moon as it passed through the system, and it just happened that Miranda was the one most easily targeted at the time, in January 1986. This image was produced by combining information from several of the individual images obtained by Voyager 2 during its flyby.

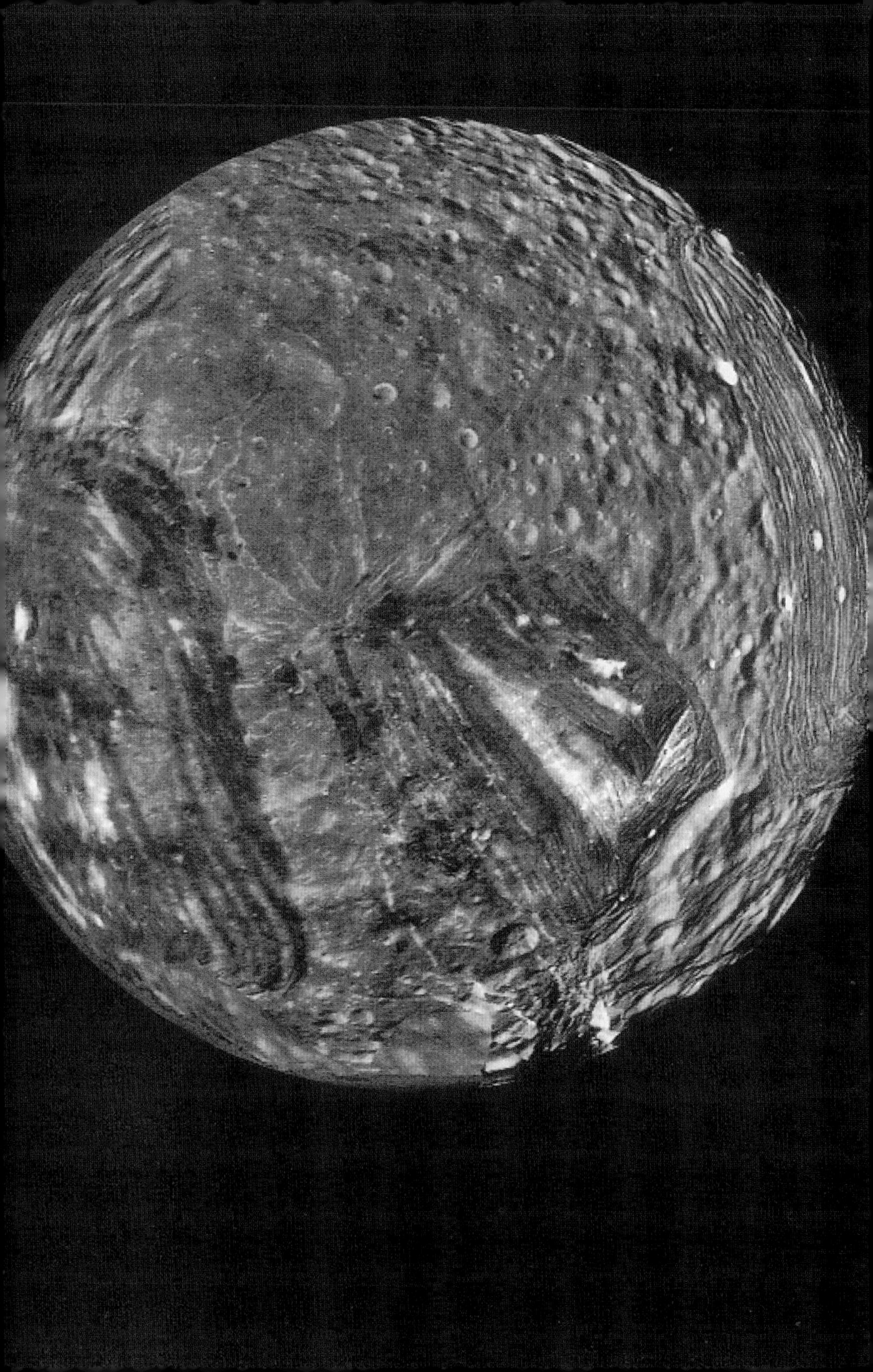

INTO THE BLUE: NEPTUNE

During 16 and 17 August 1989, Voyager 2 took a series of pictures from Neptune. This picture, taken from that sequence, shows two distinctive features in the clouds of Neptune. The dark oval-shaped feature on the left (the Great Dark Spot, shown in more detail in Plate 90) travelled around Neptune once every 18.3 hours during this period of observation. The second dark spot, at the right of the image, travelled around the planet in 16.1 hours. The image is not quite true colour, because it has been processed to enhance the visibility of small features, but Neptune really would look blue and largely featureless to the human eye.

The upper clouds of Neptune are actually made of methane, but there is a largely transparent and haze-free atmosphere above the clouds, unlike on Uranus. The deep blue colour is caused by the scattering of sunlight in the atmosphere – the same process that makes the sky look blue from the surface of the Earth. The day on Neptune lasts for 16 hours and 7 minutes. As well as a family of at least eight moons it has four faint rings.

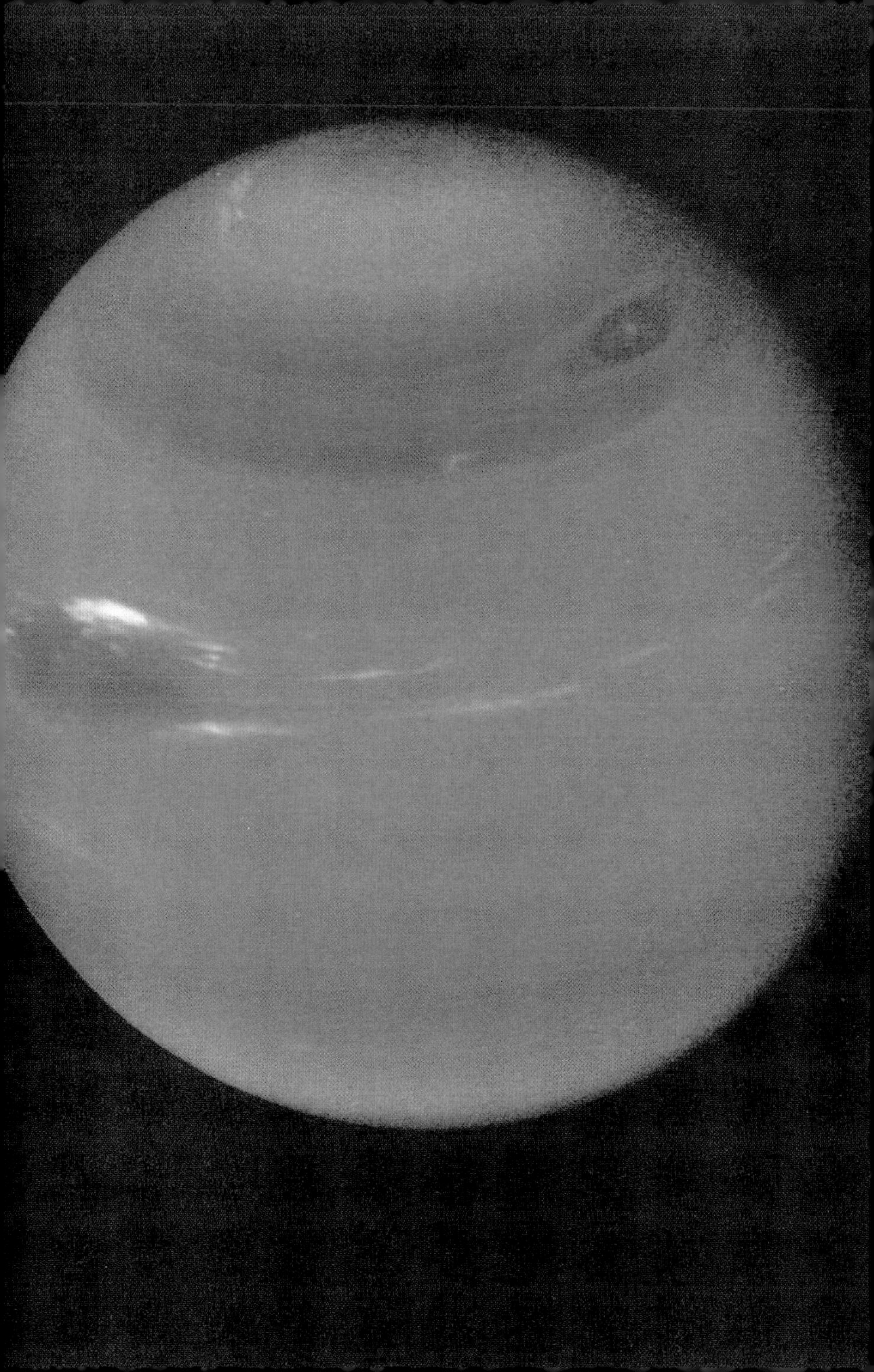

THE GREAT DARK SPOT

This Voyager 2 image of part of the surface of Neptune was obtained from a distance of 2.8 million km, and shows the Great Dark Spot in more detail. Surrounding the Spot are white clouds that rotate with it and change their structure rapidly. All these features were moving from west to east at different speeds during the period when Voyager 2 observed Neptune, in August 1989, and were clearly being carried by strong winds in the planet's atmosphere.

The Great Dark Spot was about 6,000 km across and 10,000 km long: the Earth would fit neatly inside it. It rotated anticlockwise, once every 16 days, and sat at almost exactly the same latitude on Neptune (20°S) as the Great Red Spot (see Plate 79) does on Jupiter. Both Great Spots were of similar shape and comparable in size in proportion to the diameter of their host planets. Since the exact origin of these spots is not known, nobody knows whether this is just a coincidence, or a profound feature of the structure of the giant planets. But the Great Dark Sport was not as long-lived as its Jovian counterpart: observations made by the Hubble Space Telescope in 1994 showed that it had disappeared.

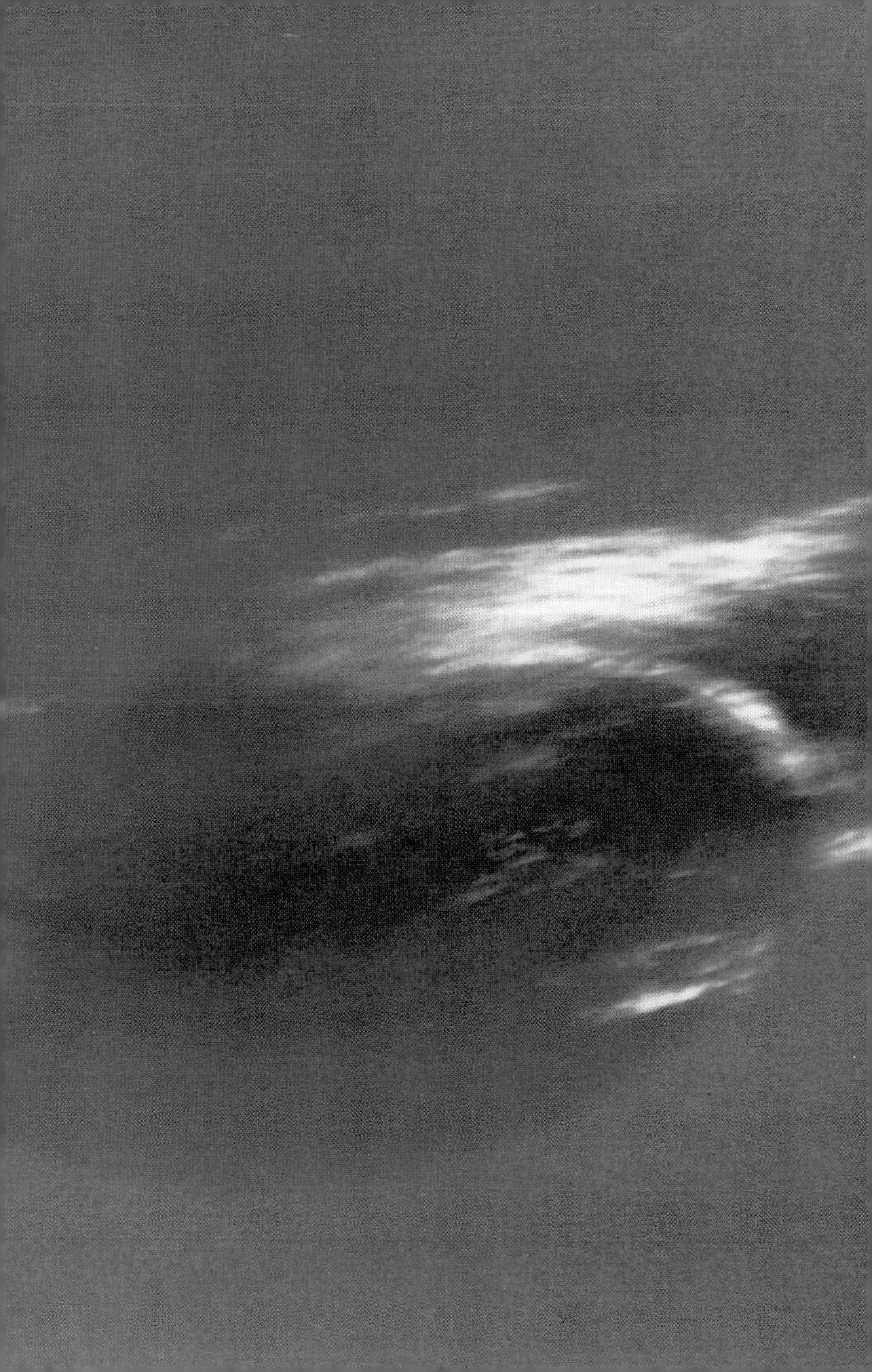

PLUTO AND CHARON

No spaceprobe has yet visited Pluto, the most remote object in the Solar System usually dignified with the name 'planet'. NASA scientists launched an unmanned mission, called New Horizons, to Pluto in January 2006. It is expected to encounter Pluto in July 2015. This picture of Pluto and its moon (or binary companion) Charon was taken by the Hubble Space Telescope on 21 February 1995. In fact, at that time Pluto was closer to the Sun than Neptune was; the highly eccentric orbit of the Pluto-Charon system takes it within Neptune's orbit for long stretches of time, including the interval from 1979 to 1999. When this photograph was taken Pluto was only 4.4 billion km (about 30 AU) from Earth, as close as it ever gets to us. This was one of the first pictures ever to show Pluto and Charon as separate, distinct disks, and it was by using images like this that astronomers determined the diameter of Pluto as 2,302 km and that of Charon as 1,186 km; the pair are separated by a distance of only 19,600 km. The temperature at the surface of Pluto is minus 223 degrees Celsius.

THE PLUTO MAP

Pluto is two-thirds the size of the Earth's Moon, but 1,200 times farther away. This makes these superficially unspectacular images (overleaf) among the most impressive achievements of observational astronomy. During late June and early July 1994, the Hubble Space Telescope took a series of photographs of Pluto as it rotated through one complete 6.4-day period. Each square picture element (pixel) in the Hubble images covers a square more than 160 km on a side on Pluto, so no feature smaller than that can be distinguished in the images. But after computer processing to clean up the pictures, astronomers have obtained the images shown here, which are maps of two opposite hemispheres of Pluto (so together they cover the entire surface of the ninth planet).

There are about a dozen main regions visible on the face of Pluto that can be distinguished, which means that it shows more large-scale contrast in its surface features than any other planet except Earth. Some of these features may be topographic structures, such as large impact craters or basins like the lunar maria. The most likely explanation of most of the pattern of bright and dark regions on the surface of Pluto, though, is that it is covered by different kinds of frost, which reflect sunlight in different degrees. In that case, these may be temporary features that migrate with the seasons. The prominent 'north polar cap' is almost certainly a seasonal feature of this kind – but since one year for Pluto lasts for 248 of our years, even seasonal features may last for a relatively long time.

And that (since we have already shown you images of comets in Plates 71 and 72) brings us to the end of our pictorial tour of the Solar System. But this is far from being the end of the story of the exploration of the Empire of the Sun, with both Cassini and a whole range of 'faster, cheaper, better' spaceprobes that will be sending back more spectacular images of the planets and moons of the Solar System as we move further in to the 21 century.

Appendices

APPENDIX 1:

PRINCIPAL PLANETARY MISSIONS, 1973-1997

Year	Month	Arrival at	Comments
1973	November	–	Mariner 10 launched
1974	March	Mercury	Mariner 10's first encounter with Mercury (two more in September 1974 and March 1975)
1975	August	–	Viking 1 launched
	September	–	Viking 2 launched
1976	June	Mars	Viking 1 arrives, lander touches down on 20 July 1976
	August	Mars	Viking 2 arrives, lander touches down on 3 September 1976
1977	August	–	Voyager 2 launched
	September	–	Voyager 1 launched
1979	March	Jupiter	Voyager 1 passes through Jovian system
	July	Jupiter	Voyager 2 passes through Jovian system
1980	November	Saturn	Voyager 1 passes through Saturnian system
1981	August	Saturn	Voyager 2 passes through Saturnian system
	October	–	Venera 13 orbiter and lander launched
	November	–	Venera 14 orbiter and lander launched
1982	March	Venus	Veneras 13 and 14 land (they survive for 127 and 57 minutes, respectively)

Year	Month	Arrival at	Comments
1985	July	–	Giotto probe launched
1986	January	Uranus	Voyager 2 passes by Uranus
	March	Halley's Comet	Giotto encounters Halley's Comet
1989	May	–	Magellan orbiter launched from Space Shuttle
	August	Neptune	Voyager 2 passes Neptune
	October	Jupiter	Galileo probe launched from Space Shuttle
1990	August	Venus	Magellan arrives at Venus and functions until October 1994
1992	July	Comet	Giotto encounters its second comet: Grigg-Skjellerup
1994	January	Moon	Clementine launched, passes by the Moon several times
1995	December	Jupiter	Galileo arrives and its probe enters the Jovian atmosphere (Galileo is still operational)
		Sun	SOHO solar observatory launched (still operational)
1996	February	–	Near Earth Asteroid Rendezvous (NEAR) launched
	November	–	Mars Global Surveyor launched
	December	–	Mars Pathfinder launched
1997	June	Mathilde	NEAR passes close to asteroid Mathilde
	July	Mars	Mars Pathfinder lands, functions for two months
	September	Mars	Mars Global Surveyor enters Mars orbit
	October	–	Cassini mission to Saturn launched

APPENDIX 2:

INTO THE FUTURE...

The golden age of planetary exploration was in the 1970s, during the space race. Between 1970 and 1978 the USA and the Soviet Union launched thirty-one successful (and attempted many other unsuccessful) missions to other planets, not including the Moon. A loss of interest in space exploration and cut-backs in budgets meant that between 1979 and 1988 only nine successful probes were launched, and six of those were Soviet missions to Venus. The 1990s, however, saw a return to the planets and a reawakening of our interest in exploring our Solar System (and beyond).

The ethos of planetary exploration has changed, though. It is no longer possible to spend huge amounts of money on massive, multi-pupose spaceprobes, building two of everything just in case one fails. The emphasis now is on smaller, faster and cheaper space exploration. The new generation of spaceprobes cost only a fraction (in real terms) of a 1970s probe, and are designed to do specific scientific jobs and to do them as efficiently and cheaply as possible. If a probe fails, it is not the disaster that it once was.

Since 1989 we have seen a new wave of explorers, many of which have featured in this book – Magellan, Galileo and Mars Pathfinder being the most important. The future, though, holds much more. Several important missions were launched at the beginning of the 21st century and many more spaceprobes are in the planning stages.

The target of much of the planetary exploration in the first part of this century is Mars, certainly the most hospitable planet from our point of view. The goal for the near future is to put humans on the red planet. Five more orbiters will join Mars Global Surveyor over the next few years, together with five landers and another rover. These explorers will search for information on the planet's past, look for evidence of life past or present, and pave the way to a manned mission which we hope will happen before too long.

A new area of research in the Solar System which will enjoy a burst of activity over the next few years is asteroids and comets. In the search for information on the early history of the Solar System, there will be two asteroid and comet flyby missions which will join NEAR and pass by a further five asteroids and comets. In addition there will be three missions to sample and return portions of a comet's nucleus to Earth, and one to return samples of an asteroid.

The rest of the Solar System has not been forgotten. The Japanese in particular are very interested in the Moon, seeing it as a possible stopping off point for the manned exploration of the Solar System, and are planning three lunar orbiters. ESA plans to return to Mercury with a probe that should go into orbit about the innermost planet in 2008 or 2009. NASA wishes to study Europa in more detail with a special orbiter which will determine the thickness of the icy crust, and find liquid water if it exists. There are also plans to visit Pluto for the first time, followed by a journey to the Kuiper Belt of comets beyond.

APPENDIX 3:

EXPLORING THE SOLAR SYSTEM ON THE INTERNET

The advent of the World Wide Web has created a host of interesting astronomical sites for the general public. As so many people have access to the Internet, either through PCs at home and work or through Internet Cafés, we decided that a list of some of the best sites on the Internet would be of use.

NASA

http://www.nasa.gov/

What more need we say? This is the NASA homepage from which it is possible to get to all parts of NASA.

Planetary exploration timeline

http://nssdc.gsfc.nasa.gov/planetary/chrono.html

A (very nearly complete) list of past and future planetary spaceprobes, with information on and pictures from many of the missions, and links to the homepages of famous, recent and ongoing missions.

NASA Photo Gallery

http://www.nasa.gov/gallery/photo/index.html

A list of links to picture collections throughout NASA and associated organisations. For images of the planets, try the 'Planetary Photojournal', while 'Welcome to the Planets' has all the information you could want about the planets and their moons.

SOHO homepage

http://sohowww.nascom.nasa.gov/

The home of the SOHO satellite has lots of information for the layman about the Sun as well as a great picture gallery.

Glossary

Anglo-Australian Telescope

A 4-metre telescope opened in 1971. Based at Siding Spring in eastern Australia, the AAT is able to observe a wealth of interesting objects unobservable from the northern hemisphere, such as the Galactic centre and the Large and Small Magellanic Clouds.

Astronomical unit (AU)

The average distance between the Earth and the Sun, about 150 million km or 93 million miles. The AU is a useful unit for describing the distances between planets.

Big Bang

The hypothetical beginning of the Universe in which the whole of space and time was created in an infinitesimally small point which has expanded outwards for the past 10-20 billion years into the Universe we know today. The phrase 'Big Bang' was originally coined by astronomer Fred Hoyle as a term of derision.

Black hole

An object that has been shrunk by gravity until its gravitational pull is so strong that nothing, not even light, can travel fast enough to escape from it.

Cepheid variable

A type of very bright star which pulses with a regular period. If the period of the pulses is known then the distance to the star can be calculated very accurately. Hence Cepheids are very useful in finding the distances to galaxies.

COBE

The COsmic Background Explorer satellite, launched in 1989 to map the fluctuations in the radiation left over after the Big Bang. As the Universe has expanded, this radiation has cooled to a temperature of only 3 degrees K (-270 degrees C).

Comet

A small body in the Solar System made up of ice and rock. Comets become visible as they near the Sun because of their tail, which is made up of material boiled off the comet by the heat of the Sun.

Dark matter

The name given to any matter that cannot be seen. As we cannot see it we do not know what it is, but we do know that it is there. As much as 90 per cent of the Universe may be made up of mysterious dark matter.

Disk galaxy

See **spiral galaxy**.

Elliptical galaxy

A round, featureless galaxy which, unlike a spiral galaxy or irregular galaxy, does not contain gas and so cannot form new stars.

ESA

The European Space Agency, which builds and launches satellites and planetary missions. In the modern spirit of international co-operation (mainly because space missions are becoming too expensive for one country alone), the ESA collaborates extensively with NASA on such projects as SOHO, Giotto and the Hubble Space Telescope.

Galaxy

A collection of maybe hundreds of billions of stars, and often gas, held together by gravity.

Galaxy cluster

A group of galaxies bound together by the force of gravity. Galaxy clusters may contain thousands of individual galaxies.

Galileo

The Galileo spacecraft (named, unsurprisingly, after Galileo Galilei), launched from the space shuttle *Atlantis* in October 1989. Following an unusual orbit, Galileo first travelled towards the Sun and used the gravity of Venus and Earth as a boost in order to reach Jupiter in late 1995.

Giotto

A joint NASA/ESA mission to study two comets, most importantly Halley's Comet. Launched in July 1985, Giotto passed within 600 km of the nucleus of Halley's Comet on 13 March 1986. In July 1992, Giotto also passed within 200 km of the comet Grigg-Skjellerup.

Gravitational lens

When light from a distant galaxy is bent by the gravitational pull of another galaxy or galaxy cluster we can sometimes see multiple images of the distant gallaxy. This effect is gravitational lensing.

Infrared

The part of the spectrum with frequencies just too long for the human eye to see.

Irregular galaxy

A galaxy which has no clear structure. Irregular galaxies seem to have been more common early in the history of the Universe.

Light year

The distance travellled by light in one year. Light travels at 300,000 km per second, and in one year covers 9.46 thousand billion km or 5.88 thousand billion miles.

Mariner 10

A NASA spacecraft which explored the inner Solar System in the mid-1970s. Mariner 10 has provided the most detailed information we have on Mercury, the inner-most planet, in a series of fly-bys, the closest passing only 327 km above the surface.

NASA

The National Aeronautics and Space Administration, the body that runs the USA's space programme. It is without doubt the best-known and most successful space programme in the world.

Nebula

A huge cloud of dust and gas, often weighing many millions of times more than the Sun. Frequently found to be the birthplace of new stars.

Neutron star

Very massive stars (greater than about eight times the mass of the Sun) end their lives as a supernova when the outer layers of the star are blown away in a massive explosion. What is left is usually a neutron star – a densely packed ball of neutrons a few kilometres across with a mass greater than that of the Sun.

NGC numbers

The NGC number is the classification number from the New General Catalogue, first published in 1888. Many objects in the sky are known by their NGC number.

Planetary nebula

At the end of a star's red giant phase its outer layers are blown away, creating a shell of dust and gas around the star known as a planetary nebula. (Planetary nebulas have nothing to do with planets, although they were once thought to, hence their name.)

Pulsar

A pulsar is a very rapidly spinning neutron star (possibly revolving thousands of times per second) with an incredibly strong magnetic field. Every time the pulsar spins round, this magnetic field beams a strong radio pulse with such regularity that when pulses were discovered they were thought to be evidence of alien intelligence.

Quasar

The core of a distant galaxy which gives out incredible amounts of energy. This energy is thought to be produced around a huge black hole in the centre of this type of galaxy, which is billions of times heavier than the Sun.

Red giant

When a star has burnt all of the hydrogen in its core, it expands before starting to burn helium. This expansion cools the surface of the star and it becomes a red giant.

ROSAT

The ROentgen SATellite, an X-ray satellite named after the discoverer of X-rays. Launched in June 1990, one of the main objectives of the mission was to map the entire sky in X-rays.

SOHO

The SOlar and Heliospheric Observatory, designed to observe the Sun continuously in ultraviolet light, looking for activity such as solar flares and sunspots.

Spectrum
When light is split up into its component colours, the result is a spectrum. In the spectra of astronomical objects, some thin bands of colour are found to be missing. These missing lines provide a great deal of information on the composition of an astronomical object which could not be found in any other way.

Spiral galaxy
A galaxy like the Milky Way, which has a thin disk of stars thousands of light years in diameter. In this disk, new stars are forming in spiral patterns, which shine brightly and give this type of galaxy their name.

Star
A mass of mostly hydrogen and helium gas which collapses together under gravity. As a star collapses it gets hot enough in the centre to begin the nuclear fusion of hydrogen into helium. This reaction creates huge amounts of energy which keeps the star shining.

Supernova
When a star more than ten times as massive as the Sun has burnt all of the hydrogen in its centre it does not expand to become a red giant, but violently ejects its outer layer in a supernova explosion, which can be seen from millions of light years away.

Ultraviolet
The part of the spectrum with frequencies just too small for the human eye to see. The atmosphere blocks out the vast majority of ultraviolet radiation from space, especially that from the Sun which can be extremely harmful.

Viking mission

The Viking 1 and 2 spacecraft were launched in 1975 to explore Mars. Each Viking contained a lander which parachuted to the surface of Mars and an orbiter which took high-resolution images of the planet's surface from orbit. The Vikings found considerable evidence that water was once common on the surface of Mars, but failed to find any evidence of life there now.

Voyager mission

The last of NASA's Mariner series of planetary explorers; Voyagers 1 and 2 were launched in late 1977 (Voyager 2 actually launched first although it arrived at Jupiter and Saturn later). The Voyager probes were designed to explore the outer Solar System, in particular the giant planets. The Voyager missions were shut down in the late 1990s.

White dwarf

The final fate of most stars is to become a white dwarf, a very dense, hot star about the size of the Earth, which slowly cools down until it is dark.

Wide Field and Planetary Camera (WF/PC)

An instrument carried on the Hubble Space Telescope, consisting of four cameras which can image a wide area in the sky in great detail. The original WF/PC1 was replaced during the 1993 HST repair mission with the improved WF/PC2, containing extra optics to counter the flaw in HST's mirror.

X-ray

A very energetic form of electromagnetic radiation which can be very harmful. Best known for their medical uses, X-rays are produced in the hot outer layers of the Sun and are (thankfully) blocked from reaching us by the atmosphere.

Picture Credits

ORIGINS

Introduction

Star trails – Credit: Copyright Anglo-Australian Observatory. Photograph by David Malin.

The 100-inch Hooker Telescope – Credit: The Observatories of the Carnegie Institution of Washington.

Edwin Hubble and the Hooker Telescope – Credit: The Observatories of the Carnegie Institution of Washington.

The Hubble Space Telescope – Credit: NASA

Distant irregular galaxies – Credit: Richard Griffiths (JHU), The Medium Deep Survey Team and NASA.

COBE all-sky map – Credit: NASA Goddard Space Flight Center and the COBE Science Working Group.

The COBE satellite – Credit: NASA Goddard Space Flight Center and the COBE Science Working Group.

The spiral galaxy M100 – Credit: NASA.

Comet Hyakutake – Credit: Copyright Luis Chinarro.

The Orion Nebula – Credit: C R O'Dell (Rice University) and NASA.

The Horsehead Nebula – Credit: Copyright Anglo-Australian Observatory. Photograph by David Malin.

PLATES

1 **The COBE four-year map**. The total data taken over the COBE mission on the fluctuations in the microwave background was assembled to produce the COBE four-year map of the sky. This is the best information we have on the structure of this radiation across the whole sky, although a new mission is planned to improve our knowledge. Credit: NASA Goddard Space Flight Center and the COBE Science Working Group.

2 **Galaxy formation simulation**. This picture shows the results of a huge supercomputer simulation carried out by the Virgo Consortium, an international group of astronomers that studies the evolution of structure in the Universe. The region of the Universe simulated in the computer world is around 2,000 trillion cubic light years in extent! Credit: The Virgo Consortium.

3 **The Lick galaxy map**. This map shows the brightest million or so galaxies visible from the northern hemisphere. The Universe is estimated to contain over a billion galaxies visible to the most powerful telescopes. Many of these galaxies are grouped into clusters, superclusters and walls of galaxies with huge voids between them. Credit: M Seldner, B L Siebers, E J Groth and P J E Peebles (*Astronomical Journal*, 82, 249, 1977).

4 **The Coma galaxy cluster**. A picture taken in X-rays by ROSAT of one of the closest giant clusters of galaxies. The hot intergalactic gas that appears in this picture has a total mass probably far greater than that of all the individual galaxies put together. In addition there may be exotic invisible matter in the cluster which has even more mass than the gas. Credit: S L Snowden, Universities Space Research Association and NASA Goddard Space Flight Center.

5 **The homes of quasars**. All of these images were taken with

the Hubble Space Telescope's WF/PC2. They reveal the faint host galaxies of these quasars which would be invisible to telescopes on Earth, allowing a study of the families of host galaxies impossible before. Credit: John Bahcall (Institute for Advanced Study, Princeton), Mike Disney (University of Wales) and NASA.

6 **The Hubble Deep Field**. This picture is formed from many WF/PC2 images taken in four colours (three in the visible spectrum and one in infrared) over 150 orbits of the Hubble Space Telescope. Credit: Robert Williams and the Hubble Deep Field Team (STScI) and NASA.

7 **A very young galaxy in the Hubble Deep Field**. This small portion of the Hubble Deep Field shows a small and unremarkable blob at its centre. This is a distant gallaxy that appears only in the infrared images. This is because the galaxy is so distant that its light has been redshifted by the expanison of the Universe so that it is unseen in visible light (the infrared light we now see was once ultraviolet light). Credit: Ken Lanzetta and Amos Yahil (State University of New York at Stony Brook) and NASA.

8 **A gravitational lens in the galaxy cluster Cl0024+1654**. By combining WF/PC2 images in red and blue light taken on 14 October 1994, this picture of the gravitational lensing of light through a galaxy cluster was created. Credit: W N Colley and E Turner (Princeton University), J A Tyson (Bell Labs, Lucent Technologies) and NASA.

9 **The massive elliptical galaxy M87**. In this picture it appears peaceful. M87, however, is secretly active, producing huge radio jets from its centre and generating thirty times more energy output in X-rays than in visible light. It has also probably attained its huge size by cannibalising many other galaxies. Credit: Copyright Anglo-Australian Observatory. Photograph by David Malin.

10 Face-on spiral NGC 2997. If we were able to go outside the Milky Way and look at it from above, it would probably look very much like NGC 2997. Spiral galaxies such as the Milky Way, M101 and NGC 2997 settled into their disk shapes early in their histories. The fact that they are still disks tells us that they have not had any violent encounters with other large galaxies as that would have destroyed their fragile structures. Credit: Copyright Anglo-Australian Observatory. Photograph by David Malin.

11 Edge-on spiral NGC 4945. Again, NGC 4945 looks very much like our own Milky Way would look if viewed side-on. The Sun would be found very near the plane of the disk, about two-thirds of the way out from the centre. Credit: Copyright Anglo-Australian Observatory. Photograph by David Malin.

12 Barred spiral NGC 1365. Although barred and unbarred spiral galaxies can look quite different, they are basicallly the same sort of galaxy. Indeed, there are theories that say that bars tend to apppear in spiral galaxies without them, but as soon as they do they become unstable and disappear again. If this is so, whether a spiral is barred or unbarred just depends on how you look at it. Credit: Anglo-Australian Observatory. Photograph by David Malin.

13 Starburst irregular galaxy NGC 1313. This galaxy lies fairly close to us, at a distance of only about 15 million light years, and was the site of Supernova 1978k (the eleventh supernova in 1978), which was discovered from its X-ray emission rather than from its visible light. Credit: Copyright Anglo-Australian Observatory. Photograph by David Malin.

14 The spiral galaxy M101 in ultraviolet light. The space shuttle *Endeavour* carried the Ultraviolet Imaging Telescope during the Astro-2 mission, which was used to image a number of interesting astronomical objects. M101 is one of the largest spiral galaxies – its diameter is nearly three times that of the Milky Way. Credit: NASA.

15 **The Large Magellanic Cloud (LMC) in ultraviolet light**. The LMC, an active star-forming irregular galaxy, is in orbit about the Milky Way and is slowly being dragged down into the Milky Way. At some point in the distant future, the LMC will eventuallly be disrupted and merged into it. This is believed to have happened to other small galaxies many times in the Milky Way's past – like all large galaxies, it is thought to be something of a cannibal. Credit: NASA.

16 **Globular cluster 47 Tucanae**. Globular clusters are among the most spectacular sights that it is possible to see with the eye through small telescopes. Most globular clusters are closer to the Galactic centre than the Sun and can be seen only from the southern hemisphere. However, there are a number which are easily visible from the northern hemisphere. Globular clusters lie in a spherical halo about the Galaxy that stretches over 300,000 light years from the centre. Credit: Copyright Anglo-Australian Observatory. Photograph by David Malin.

17 **Open cluster NGC 6520 and a dark nebula**. All of the Milky Way's gas, dust and young stars lie in the middle of the disk of the Galaxy. Hence the youngest objects are almost always found to lie exactly on the Galactic equator (in the visible band of the Milky Way overhead). Credit: Anglo-Australian Observatory. Photograph by David Malin.

18 **The Milky Way in infrared light**. This image was made by the COBE satellite and shows a disk of stars and dust very similar to that of NGC 4945 (Plate 11). Credit: NASA Goddard Space Flight Center and the COBE Science Working Group.

19 **The band of the Milky Way across the Galactic centre**. This view of the Galactic centre is visible only from the southern hemisphere. It is a visible light picture of the central area of Plate 18. Near the centre of this picture, but obscured by dust and gas, is a strong X-ray source: Sagittarius A. This source may be associated with a giant black hole in the centre of the Milky Way. Credit: Copyright Anglo-Australian Observatory. Photograph by David Malin.

20 **The Cone Nebula**. The nebula is 4,500 light years away in the southern constellation of Monoceros. Credit: Copyright Anglo-Australian Observatory. Photgraph David Malin.

21 **The Tarantula Nebula**. The nebula contains a young star cluster (that might well be a young globular cluster) known as NGC 2070. In the heart of NGC 2070 is R136. For many years R136 was thought to be a supermassive star with a mass more than a thousand times greater than that of the Sun. In the late 1980s, R136 was finally resolved as a tiny star cluster 1 light year across, containing hundreds of stars. Many of these stars will become supernovas, blowing the Tarantula Nebula away, leaving just the stars of NGC 2070. Credit: Anglo-Australian Observatory. Photograph by David Malin.

22 **The Lagoon Nebula**. The HST's WF/PC2 has revealed turbulence in the gas of the Lagoon Nebula. Again, the HST has been able to resolve details which would have been impossible to see from the surface of the Earth due to the effects of the atmosphere. The different colours in this image correspond to light from different types of atoms: red from ionised sodium (sodium atoms that have lost some electrons), blue from ionised oxygen and green from ionised hydrogen. Credit: A Caulet (Space Telescope European Co-ordinating Facility, ESA) and NASA.

23 **A starburst in galaxy NGC 253.** The WF/PC2 took this picture of a starburst in the centre of spiral galaxy NGC 253. The analysis of the starbirth in this galaxy shows that stars almost always seem to form in clusters, rather than individually. Credit: Carnegie Institute of Washington and

NASA.

24 **A giant region of starbirth in the galaxy NGC 604**. This image was taken by the Hubble Space Telescope's WF/PC2 on 17 January 1995. Pictures were taken in many different colours. The changes in the images between different colours can tell us about the physics of the gas in which the young stars are embedded. Credit: Hui Yang (University of Illinois) and NASA.

25 **Cometary globule CG4**. The most spectacular picture of a cometary globule must be this of CG4, due to the chance alignment with the spiral galaxy in the picture. CG4 is rather faint, and the exposure time required to record it well has left the spiral galaxy slightly overexposed. Credit: Copyright Anglo-Australian Observatory. Photograph by David Malin.

26 **Light echoes around Supernova 1987A**. Since the explosion of Supernova 1987A, it has become one of the most observed objects in the sky. The stuudy of how the blast wave from the supernova propagates through space tells us a lot about the conditions and energy in the initial explosion. This pipcture was taken with the WF/PC2 in February 1994. Credit: Christopher Burrows (ESA/STScI) and NASA.

27 **Supernova 1987A: before and after**. It was only after Sanduleak -69° 202 exploded as Supernova 1987A that astronomers became interested in the star. This supernova was the closest since modern astronomy began and is visible to the naked eye (only in the southern hemisphere, however). The original star was thought to have been about twenty times more massive than the Sun and only a few million years old. Credit: Anglo-Australian Observatory. Photograph by David Malin.

28 **The Crab Nebula**. This image was taken on 5 November 1995 by the WF/PC2 on the Hubble Space Telescope. The image was taken in only a small band of colours corresponding to yellow light (the red colour is arbitrary, but helps the human eye see some of the detailed ripples in the nebula). Credit: Jeff Hester and Paul Scowen (Arizona State University) and NASA.

29 The Vela and Puppis supernova remnants from ROSAT. These two supernova occurred so recently in astronomical history that the temperatures of the gas blown out of them are still incredibly high. Superheated gases such as these (known as plasmas) radiate very strongly in the X-ray band, making X-ray observations a good method of finding supernova remnants that may be invisible normally (unlike these, which are very obvious). Credit: Bernard Aschenbach, Max-Planck-Institut fuer Extra-terrestrische Physik and NASA Goddard Space Flight Centre.

30 A family portrait of Jupiter. This Voyager 1 picture taken in 1979 shows the massive planet Jupiter together with three of the four Galilean moons: Io, Europa and Callisto. Jupiter's Great Red Spot is also clearly visible in the planet's southern hemisphere. Credit: NASA Jet Propulsion Laboratory.

31 Jupiter's moon Io. When the Galileo spacecraft reached Jupiter it released a probe into the planet's upper atmosphere; the spacecraft then began an extended tour of a number of Jupiter's moons. Its first target in late 1996 was Io. It revealed many changes in the surface of the moon since it was first studied in detail by the Voyager missions nearly two decades before. The changes are caused by the continuous and violent volcanic activity. Credit: NASA Jet Propulsion Laboratory.

32 Saturn from Voyager 1. This image of Saturn was taken by the Voyager 1 spacecraft just four days after its closest approach to the planet in November 1980. The spacecraft was looking back at the planet as it moved onwards past some of the Saturnian moons towards the outer Solar

System. Credit: NASA Jet Propulsion Laboratory.

33 A global view of Mars from the Viking orbiter. This view of the Cerberus hemisphere of Mars is a montage of 104 images taken by the Viking 1 orbiter. The picture shows well what Mars would look like from a high orbit, lacking only a little haze around the edges that would be caused by the thin Martian atmosphere. Credit: NASA Jet Propulsion Laboratory.

34 A radar map of Venus. This view of the surface of Venus covers the entire northern hemisphere with the north pole at the centre. Most of the radar images that make up this map come from the Magellan spacecraft, which mapped 98 per cent of Venus. The gaps have been filled in with data from the Soviet Venera 15 mission and the Pioneer Venus Orbiter along with some imformation from the huge Arecibo radio telescope in Puerto Rico. Credit: NASA Jet Propulsion Laboratory.

35 Mercury from Mariner 10. The Mariner 10 mission has given us the most detailed information on the planet Mercury – a small, battered world. Mariner 10 made three fly-bys of Mercury and was able to map about one-third of the planet's surface, revealing a very cratered world. Credit: NASA Jet Propulsion Laboratory.

36 The Sun from the SOHO satellite. This image was taken in the extreme ultraviolet light of the Sun (light so energetic it is nearly X-rays) by the SOHO (SOlar and Heliospheric Observatory) satellite. This satellite is positioned 1.5 million km away, between the Sun and the Earth where the gravity of the two bodies cancel each other out (a Lagrangian point) and where it can observe the Sun continuously. Credit: NASA and ESA.

37 Halley's Comet from Giotto. The Giotto spacecraft passed close to the nucleus of this most famous of comets in mid-

1986. For the first time a comet's nucleus could be imaged and the contents of its tail analysed from close quarters. Credit: NASA National Space Science Data Center and ESA.

38 **Asteroid Ida and its moon Dactyl**. The asteroid Ida orbits in the asteroid belt between Mars and Jupiter and was the 243rd asteroid to be discovered. Galileo passed within 11,000 km of Ida in August 1993 on its way to Jupiter, providing only the second close encounter of a spacecraft with an asteroid. Credit: NASA Jet Propulsion Laboratory.

39 **The Earth-Moon system**. This picture was taken by the Galileo spacecraft as it passed Earth for the second time in December 1992 before starting its three-year journey to Jupiter. It was taken from a distance of 6.2 million km (about sixteen times the Earth-Moon distance). Credit: NASA Jet Propulsion Laboratory.

40 **The Moon in false colour**. This image is made up of fifty-three pictures taken by Galileo on the same fly-by of Earth as for Plate 39. The images were taken through three colour filters, which show how different areas of the Moon reflect different amounts of light of each colour. The different reflective properties provide clues as to the composition and age of these areas. Credit: NASA Jet Propulsion Laboratory.

41 **The Earth from space**. This picture agains comes from the Galileo spacecraft which has provided some of the most stunning pictures of the planets since the Voyager missions. It was taken at about 14.10 GMT on 10 December 1990 on its first Earth fly-by; Galileo then passed through the inner Solar System before returning to Earth two years later for another fly-by. Credit: NASA Jet Propulsion Laboratory.

42 **An impact crater in Namibia**. This picture is another radar image, similar to that of Venus (Plate 34), but this time of a region of Earth. This image was taken from the space shuttle's Spaceborne Imaging Radar, part of NASA's Mission to Planet Earth project. Satellite-based observations of the Earth are revealing much about the history of the Earth, and providing evidence of humankind's huge influence upon the planet. Credit: NASA Jet Propulsion Laboratory.

EMPIRE OF THE SUN

All pictures are courtesy of NASA except for the following: Page 169 © Jeremy Maris; Page 163, R Beebe (NMSU) and NASA; Plate 45, courtesy of SOHO/UVCS and EIT consortia; Plate 46, courtesy of SOHO/EIT consortium (SOHO is a project of international co-operation between ESA and NASA); Plate 53, SeaWiF project, NSAS; Plate 91, R Albrecht (NASA/ESA Space Telescope European Co-ordinating Facility) and NASA; Plate 92, A Stern (SwRI), M Brie (Lowell Observatory), NASA and ESA.

Index

INDEX

Page numbers in italics refer to illustrations